SYSTEMS OF LIFE

VOLUME 2

Anne Roberts and Peter Gardiner

First edition 1993
Reprinted 1994

Published by
Macmillan Magazines Ltd
4 Little Essex Street
London WC2R 3LF

Companies and representatives throughout the world.
Printed in the UK

Macmillan Magazines Ltd

ISBN 0-333-61055-5

CONTENTS

INTRODUCTION

Systems of Life is an authoritative, carefully researched and beautifully drawn series which has been running in *Nursing Times* since 1975. It is painstakingly put together by a highly experienced team: desk editor Jean Cullinan, illustrator Peter Gardiner and writer Anne Roberts.

What readers seem to value most about it are the attractiveness and clarity of the drawings and the easy-to-follow text. It is a good example of what *Nursing Times* tries to do every week for its readers – present complex professional ideas and issues in a no-nonsense and accessible form.

Systems of Life certainly gathers new fans with each year that goes by. Students find it invaluable when revising; tutors and ward managers alike use it to compile effective learning aids.

Readers whose knowledge of anatomy and physiology has grown a little rusty find it a helpful tool, as does any professional who wants to learn or keep up to date.

Whether you are a regular reader or one who is discovering Systems of Life for the first time, I hope you will find this collection interesting, stimulating and useful.

John Gilbert
Editor, *Nursing Times*

BONE AND BONES

The bones forming the skeleton give support and shape to the body and make movement possible.
They also protect soft organs, form a store of calcium and phosphate and manufacture blood cells within their marrow.

The bones of the skull protect the brain.

The bone marrow manufactures red blood cells, some white blood cells and the platelets.

The skeleton is subdivided into:

— the axial skeleton: the skull, spine and bones of the thorax

— the appendicular skeleton: the upper and lower limbs

— the shoulder and pelvic girdles, which join the two together.

Most of the body's calcium and phosphate is stored in bones.

Limb bones provide attachments for muscles and act as levers during movement.

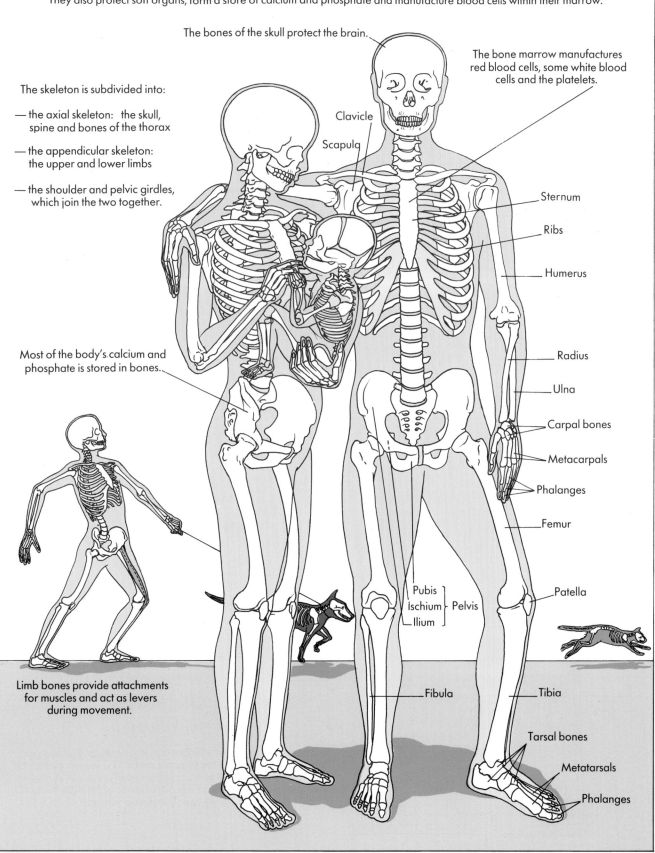

Clavicle

Scapula

Sternum

Ribs

Humerus

Radius

Ulna

Carpal bones

Metacarpals

Phalanges

Femur

Patella

Pubis
Ischium } Pelvis
Ilium

Fibula

Tibia

Tarsal bones

Metatarsals

Phalanges

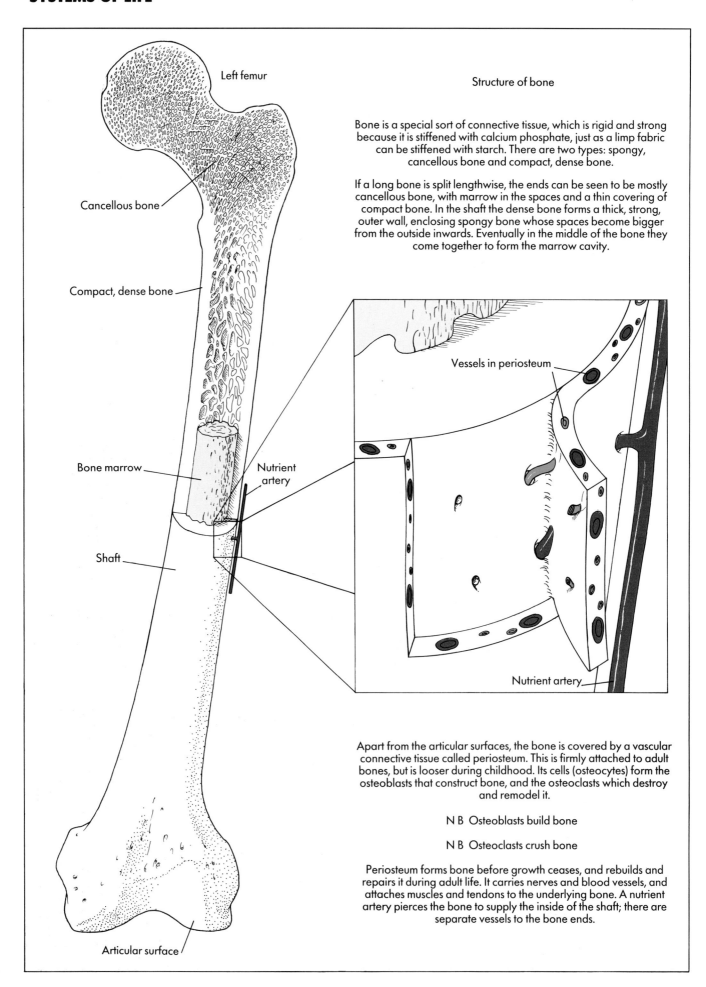

Left femur

Cancellous bone

Compact, dense bone

Bone marrow

Nutrient artery

Shaft

Articular surface

Structure of bone

Bone is a special sort of connective tissue, which is rigid and strong because it is stiffened with calcium phosphate, just as a limp fabric can be stiffened with starch. There are two types: spongy, cancellous bone and compact, dense bone.

If a long bone is split lengthwise, the ends can be seen to be mostly cancellous bone, with marrow in the spaces and a thin covering of compact bone. In the shaft the dense bone forms a thick, strong, outer wall, enclosing spongy bone whose spaces become bigger from the outside inwards. Eventually in the middle of the bone they come together to form the marrow cavity.

Vessels in periosteum

Nutrient artery

Apart from the articular surfaces, the bone is covered by a vascular connective tissue called periosteum. This is firmly attached to adult bones, but is looser during childhood. Its cells (osteocytes) form the osteoblasts that construct bone, and the osteoclasts which destroy and remodel it.

N B Osteoblasts build bone

N B Osteoclasts crush bone

Periosteum forms bone before growth ceases, and rebuilds and repairs it during adult life. It carries nerves and blood vessels, and attaches muscles and tendons to the underlying bone. A nutrient artery pierces the bone to supply the inside of the shaft; there are separate vessels to the bone ends.

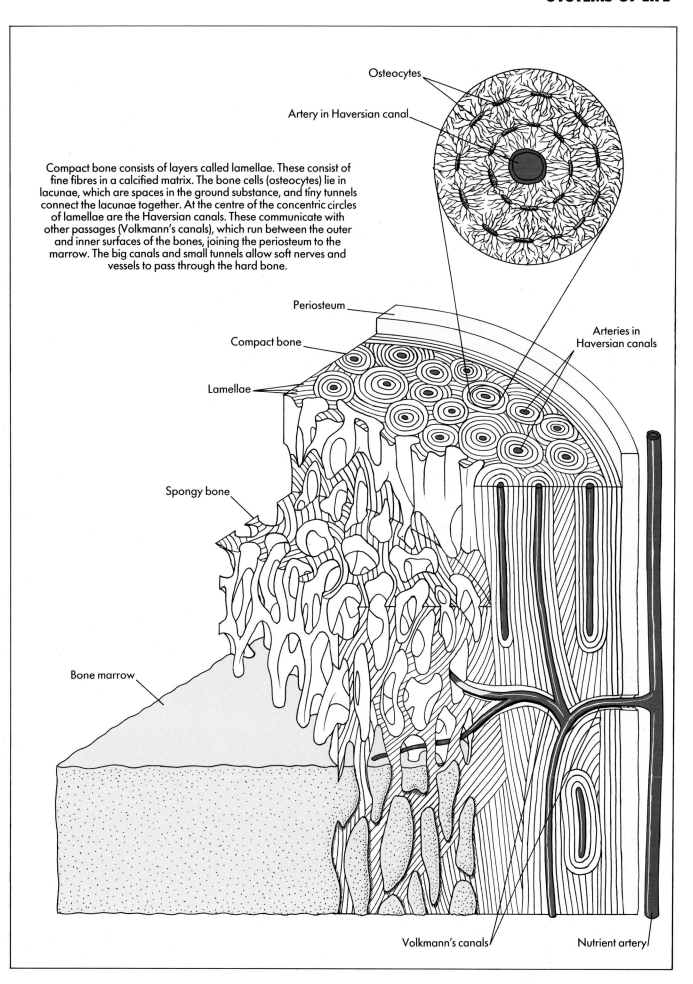

Osteocytes

Artery in Haversian canal

Compact bone consists of layers called lamellae. These consist of fine fibres in a calcified matrix. The bone cells (osteocytes) lie in lacunae, which are spaces in the ground substance, and tiny tunnels connect the lacunae together. At the centre of the concentric circles of lamellae are the Haversian canals. These communicate with other passages (Volkmann's canals), which run between the outer and inner surfaces of the bones, joining the periosteum to the marrow. The big canals and small tunnels allow soft nerves and vessels to pass through the hard bone.

Periosteum

Compact bone

Arteries in Haversian canals

Lamellae

Spongy bone

Bone marrow

Volkmann's canals

Nutrient artery

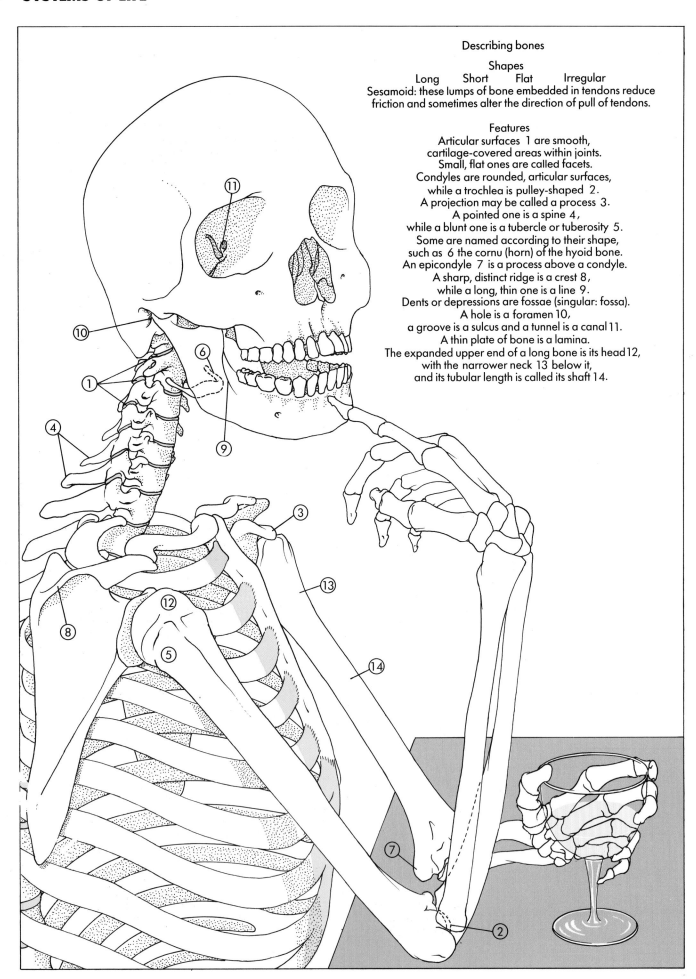

Describing bones

Shapes
Long   Short   Flat   Irregular
Sesamoid: these lumps of bone embedded in tendons reduce
friction and sometimes alter the direction of pull of tendons.

Features
Articular surfaces 1 are smooth,
cartilage-covered areas within joints.
Small, flat ones are called facets.
Condyles are rounded, articular surfaces,
while a trochlea is pulley-shaped 2.
A projection may be called a process 3.
A pointed one is a spine 4,
while a blunt one is a tubercle or tuberosity 5.
Some are named according to their shape,
such as 6 the cornu (horn) of the hyoid bone.
An epicondyle 7 is a process above a condyle.
A sharp, distinct ridge is a crest 8,
while a long, thin one is a line 9.
Dents or depressions are fossae (singular: fossa).
A hole is a foramen 10,
a groove is a sulcus and a tunnel is a canal 11.
A thin plate of bone is a lamina.
The expanded upper end of a long bone is its head 12,
with the narrower neck 13 below it,
and its tubular length is called its shaft 14.

Ossification (bone formation)

Some bones, such as the facial bones, the components of the vault of the skull and the clavicles, start to form directly in embryonic mesenchyme. Because the mesenchyme forms a membrane-like layer, this is called intramembranous ossification, and bones formed in this way are membrane bones. The first centres of ossification appear in the clavicle between the 5th and 6th week of intrauterine life.

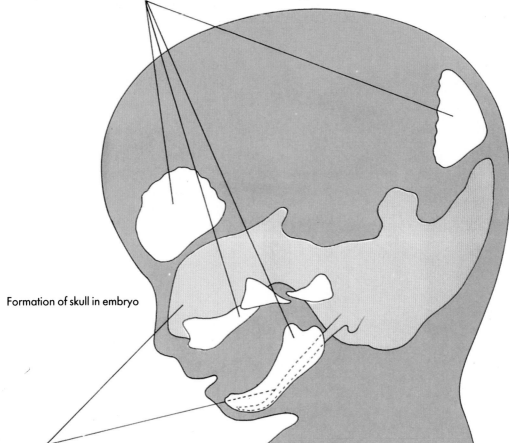

Formation of skull in embryo

Cartilage is formed in the remaining skeletal mesenchyme, and the rest of the bones develop using it as 'scaffolding'; this is intracartilaginous ossification. While this is happening, the largely cartilaginous skeleton supports the young, developing body and grows with it until permanent bone formation is completed after puberty.

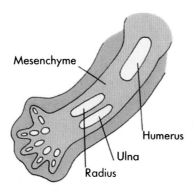

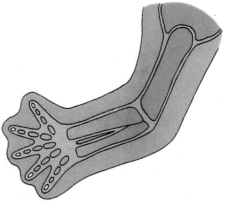

Mesenchyme

Humerus

Ulna

Radius

Embryo at beginning of
6th week — actual size

Upper limb at beginning of
6th week — cartilaginous
skeleton starting to form

Upper limb at end of 6th week
— cartilaginous skeleton completed

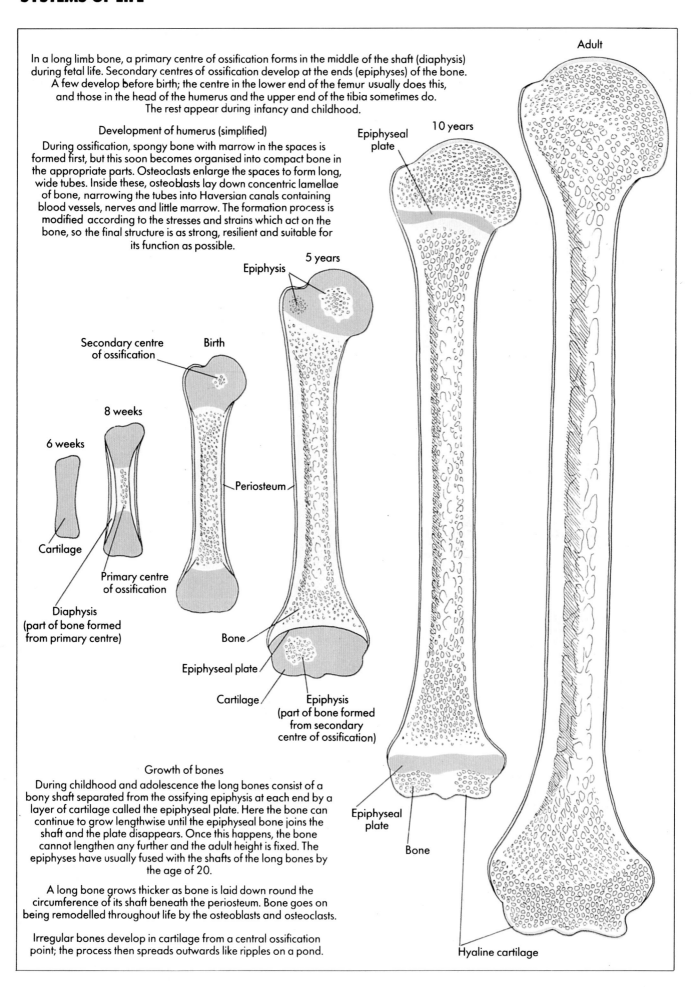

In a long limb bone, a primary centre of ossification forms in the middle of the shaft (diaphysis) during fetal life. Secondary centres of ossification develop at the ends (epiphyses) of the bone. A few develop before birth; the centre in the lower end of the femur usually does this, and those in the head of the humerus and the upper end of the tibia sometimes do. The rest appear during infancy and childhood.

Development of humerus (simplified)

During ossification, spongy bone with marrow in the spaces is formed first, but this soon becomes organised into compact bone in the appropriate parts. Osteoclasts enlarge the spaces to form long, wide tubes. Inside these, osteoblasts lay down concentric lamellae of bone, narrowing the tubes into Haversian canals containing blood vessels, nerves and little marrow. The formation process is modified according to the stresses and strains which act on the bone, so the final structure is as strong, resilient and suitable for its function as possible.

Adult

10 years

Epiphyseal plate

5 years

Epiphysis

Birth

Secondary centre of ossification

8 weeks

6 weeks

Cartilage

Primary centre of ossification

Diaphysis (part of bone formed from primary centre)

Periosteum

Bone

Epiphyseal plate

Cartilage

Epiphysis (part of bone formed from secondary centre of ossification)

Epiphyseal plate

Bone

Hyaline cartilage

Growth of bones

During childhood and adolescence the long bones consist of a bony shaft separated from the ossifying epiphysis at each end by a layer of cartilage called the epiphyseal plate. Here the bone can continue to grow lengthwise until the epiphyseal bone joins the shaft and the plate disappears. Once this happens, the bone cannot lengthen any further and the adult height is fixed. The epiphyses have usually fused with the shafts of the long bones by the age of 20.

A long bone grows thicker as bone is laid down round the circumference of its shaft beneath the periosteum. Bone goes on being remodelled throughout life by the osteoblasts and osteoclasts.

Irregular bones develop in cartilage from a central ossification point; the process then spreads outwards like ripples on a pond.

The bones and calcium metabolism

A healthy adult body contains about 1 kilogram of calcium, nearly all of it in the skeleton (99%). However, the remaining 10 grams is very important because it affects the body's metabolism. Calcium affects blood clotting, muscle contraction, membrane permeability and a variety of enzyme reactions.

40% of blood calcium is bound to protein, and only the unbound ionised portion is metabolically active. The amount of protein-binding varies with the acid-base state of the body. For instance, someone in a state of alkalosis because of overbreathing has increased protein-binding and therefore a lower level of active, ionised calcium. He may therefore develop signs of hypocalcaemia, such as tetany.

Body calcium is controlled by several interacting factors. These include:

— parathormone, produced by the parathyroid glands. These are four glands about the size and shape of a baked bean, lying behind the thyroid gland in the neck. Parathormone is produced in response to a fall in blood calcium; it then helps to raise it

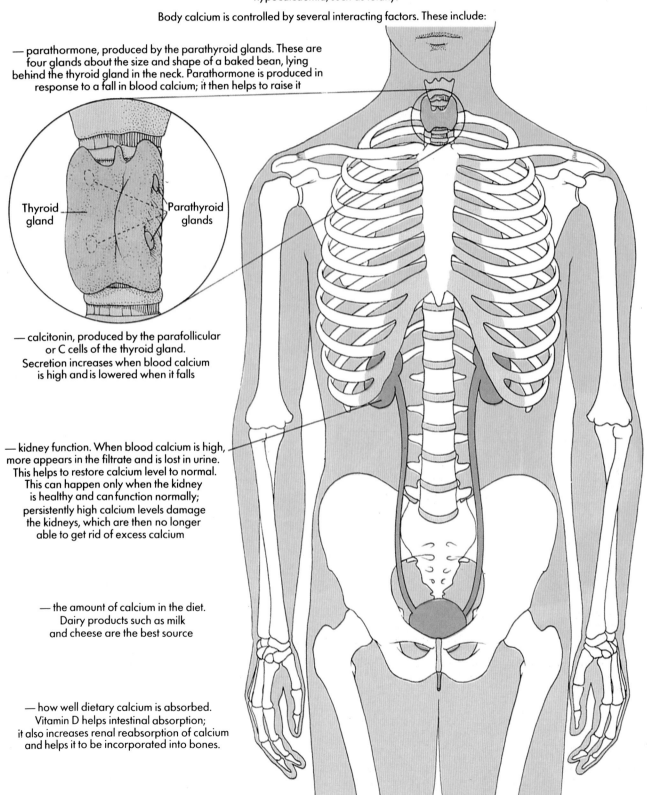

Thyroid gland

Parathyroid glands

— calcitonin, produced by the parafollicular or C cells of the thyroid gland. Secretion increases when blood calcium is high and is lowered when it falls

— kidney function. When blood calcium is high, more appears in the filtrate and is lost in urine. This helps to restore calcium level to normal. This can happen only when the kidney is healthy and can function normally; persistently high calcium levels damage the kidneys, which are then no longer able to get rid of excess calcium

— the amount of calcium in the diet. Dairy products such as milk and cheese are the best source

— how well dietary calcium is absorbed. Vitamin D helps intestinal absorption; it also increases renal reabsorption of calcium and helps it to be incorporated into bones.

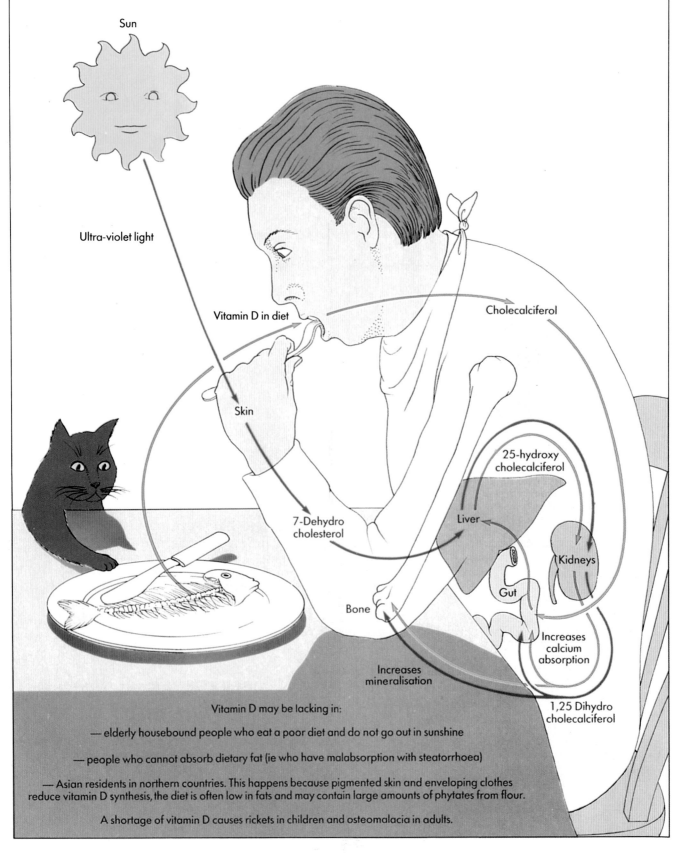

Vitamin D metabolism

Vitamin D can be synthesised in the skin by the action of ultra-violet light on a precursor. In northern countries the amount of vitamin D the body can make in this way is often inadequate; then dietary vitamin D becomes important. It is fat-soluble and is found in fish liver oils, 'fatty fish' such as sardines, herrings and tuna and in fortified margarine. The liver and kidneys metabolise vitamin D made in the skin or absorbed from the diet into an active form.

Sun

Ultra-violet light

Vitamin D in diet

Cholecalciferol

Skin

25-hydroxy cholecalciferol

7-Dehydro cholesterol

Liver

Kidneys

Gut

Bone

Increases calcium absorption

Increases mineralisation

1,25 Dihydro cholecalciferol

Vitamin D may be lacking in:

— elderly housebound people who eat a poor diet and do not go out in sunshine

— people who cannot absorb dietary fat (ie who have malabsorption with steatorrhoea)

— Asian residents in northern countries. This happens because pigmented skin and enveloping clothes reduce vitamin D synthesis, the diet is often low in fats and may contain large amounts of phytates from flour.

A shortage of vitamin D causes rickets in children and osteomalacia in adults.

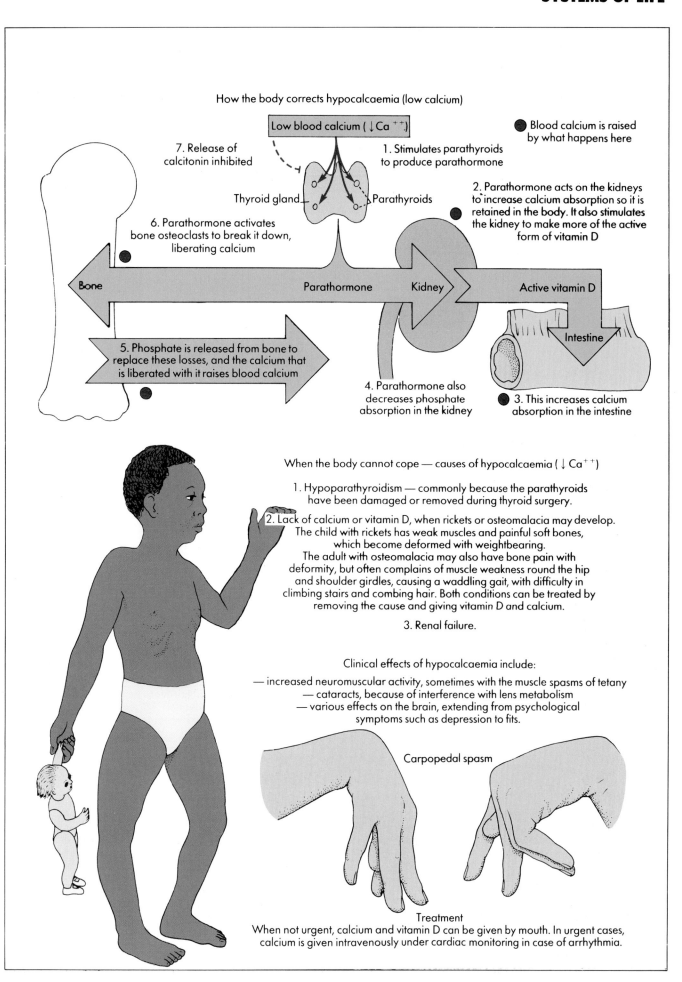

How the body corrects hypocalcaemia (low calcium)

Low blood calcium ($\downarrow Ca^{++}$)

● Blood calcium is raised by what happens here

7. Release of calcitonin inhibited

1. Stimulates parathyroids to produce parathormone

Thyroid gland — Parathyroids

2. Parathormone acts on the kidneys to increase calcium absorption so it is retained in the body. It also stimulates the kidney to make more of the active form of vitamin D

6. Parathormone activates bone osteoclasts to break it down, liberating calcium

Bone

Parathormone

Kidney

Active vitamin D

Intestine

5. Phosphate is released from bone to replace these losses, and the calcium that is liberated with it raises blood calcium

4. Parathormone also decreases phosphate absorption in the kidney

3. This increases calcium absorption in the intestine

When the body cannot cope — causes of hypocalcaemia ($\downarrow Ca^{++}$)

1. Hypoparathyroidism — commonly because the parathyroids have been damaged or removed during thyroid surgery.

2. Lack of calcium or vitamin D, when rickets or osteomalacia may develop. The child with rickets has weak muscles and painful soft bones, which become deformed with weightbearing.
The adult with osteomalacia may also have bone pain with deformity, but often complains of muscle weakness round the hip and shoulder girdles, causing a waddling gait, with difficulty in climbing stairs and combing hair. Both conditions can be treated by removing the cause and giving vitamin D and calcium.

3. Renal failure.

Clinical effects of hypocalcaemia include:

— increased neuromuscular activity, sometimes with the muscle spasms of tetany
— cataracts, because of interference with lens metabolism
— various effects on the brain, extending from psychological symptoms such as depression to fits.

Carpopedal spasm

Treatment
When not urgent, calcium and vitamin D can be given by mouth. In urgent cases, calcium is given intravenously under cardiac monitoring in case of arrhythmia.

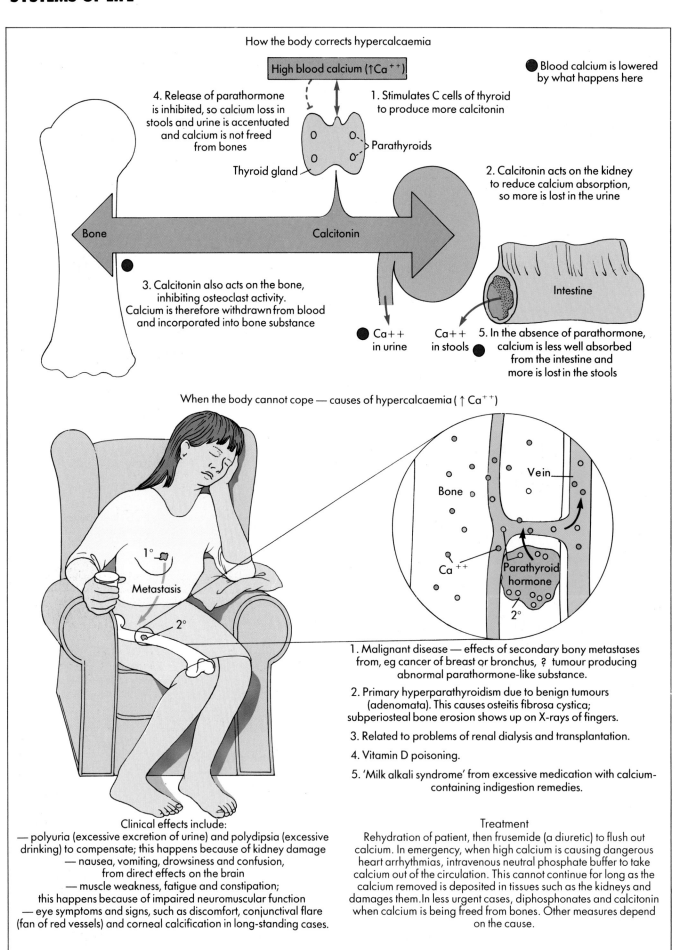

How the body corrects hypercalcaemia

High blood calcium ($\uparrow Ca^{++}$)

● Blood calcium is lowered by what happens here

4. Release of parathormone is inhibited, so calcium loss in stools and urine is accentuated and calcium is not freed from bones

1. Stimulates C cells of thyroid to produce more calcitonin

Parathyroids

Thyroid gland

2. Calcitonin acts on the kidney to reduce calcium absorption, so more is lost in the urine

Bone

Calcitonin

3. Calcitonin also acts on the bone, inhibiting osteoclast activity. Calcium is therefore withdrawn from blood and incorporated into bone substance

Intestine

● $Ca++$ in urine

$Ca++$ in stools ●

5. In the absence of parathormone, calcium is less well absorbed from the intestine and more is lost in the stools

When the body cannot cope — causes of hypercalcaemia ($\uparrow Ca^{++}$)

1°

Metastasis

2°

Vein

Bone

Ca^{++}

Parathyroid hormone

2°

1. Malignant disease — effects of secondary bony metastases from, eg cancer of breast or bronchus, ? tumour producing abnormal parathormone-like substance.

2. Primary hyperparathyroidism due to benign tumours (adenomata). This causes osteitis fibrosa cystica; subperiosteal bone erosion shows up on X-rays of fingers.

3. Related to problems of renal dialysis and transplantation.

4. Vitamin D poisoning.

5. 'Milk alkali syndrome' from excessive medication with calcium-containing indigestion remedies.

Clinical effects include:
— polyuria (excessive excretion of urine) and polydipsia (excessive drinking) to compensate; this happens because of kidney damage
— nausea, vomiting, drowsiness and confusion, from direct effects on the brain
— muscle weakness, fatigue and constipation; this happens because of impaired neuromuscular function
— eye symptoms and signs, such as discomfort, conjunctival flare (fan of red vessels) and corneal calcification in long-standing cases.

Treatment
Rehydration of patient, then frusemide (a diuretic) to flush out calcium. In emergency, when high calcium is causing dangerous heart arrhythmias, intravenous neutral phosphate buffer to take calcium out of the circulation. This cannot continue for long as the calcium removed is deposited in tissues such as the kidneys and damages them. In less urgent cases, diphosphonates and calcitonin when calcium is being freed from bones. Other measures depend on the cause.

Fractures

A decalcified bone remnant becomes so soft it can be tied in a knot. If instead the protein matrix is dissolved, the mineral portion alone is very brittle and crumbles easily. The combination of protein matrix and calcium is strong and resilient, but can still be broken (fractured) by excessive force. An abnormal bone may break very easily.

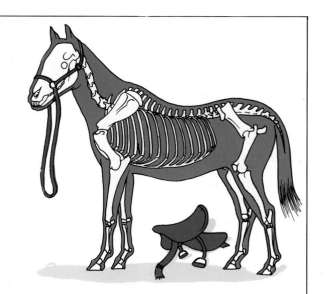

Types of Fracture
— Simple: has no skin wound communicating with the break. This type is not necessarily easy to treat
— Compound: a skin wound communicates with the fracture
— Comminuted: the bone is broken into more than two fragments
— Greenstick or incomplete: the bone is broken on the convex side but only buckled on the other, and the periosteum is not torn. This type occurs in children.
— Pathological: in a bone weakened by secondary tumour deposits, osteoporosis or other bone disease.

Signs of fracture
— Severe pain and swelling, sometimes with deformity, over a bone after an injury

— abnormal mobility

— crepitus (grating of the bone ends against each other)

} These should *not* be sought deliberately, as the attempt to do so may worsen tissue damage

In addition, some fractures bear the name of the person who first described them. Examples are Pott's fracture, a fracture dislocation of the ankle joint, and Colles' fracture, a fracture of the lower radius with posterior displacement. Others are named according to the circumstances in which they commonly happen, such as the March fracture, a fracture of the third metatarsal following an unusual amount of strenuous walking.

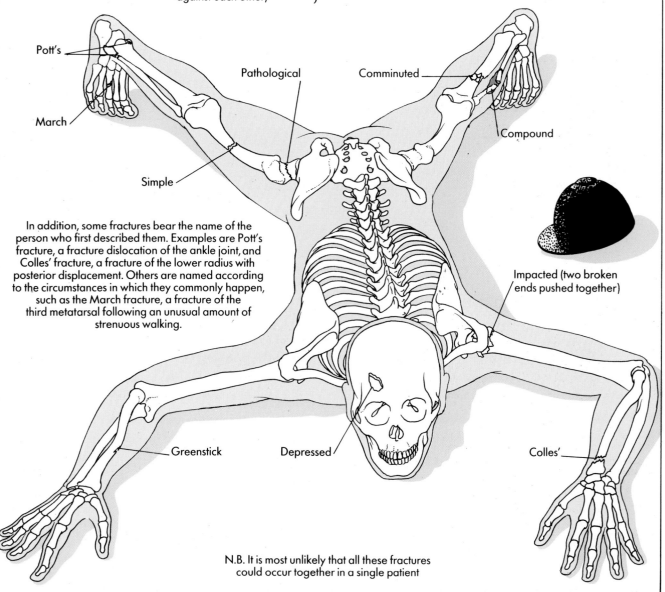

Pott's

March

Pathological

Comminuted

Compound

Simple

Impacted (two broken ends pushed together)

Greenstick

Depressed

Colles'

N.B. It is most unlikely that all these fractures could occur together in a single patient

How a fracture heals

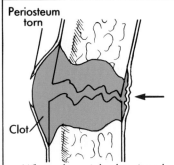

Periosteum torn

Clot

When a bone is broken, it and the soft tissues around it are both damaged. The periosteum is stripped off on the side opposite to the impact; its blood vessels rupture and a haematoma (clot) accumulates between the broken ends.

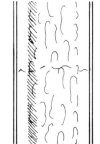

Granulation tissue

Callus

As healing starts, fibres grow across through the clot to bridge the gap.

Osteocytes move in to form callus, a soft form of bone which joins the ends together.

The callus is gradually hardened and shaped into replacement bone.

Principles of Treatment

Reduction and immobilisation help natural healing; rehabilitation aims to restore function. Reduction restores the bones to their proper position; this usually involves moving the bones in the opposite direction to the force that caused the fracture. Reduction can be:

— closed, when the bone ends are pulled apart before being restored to their normal position

— open, requiring an operation which may convert a simple fracture into a compound one. This is necessary when closed reduction fails, when soft tissue lies between the bone ends, or when internal fixation will be necessary.

Immobilisation may involve:
— external fixation, as with a plaster cast

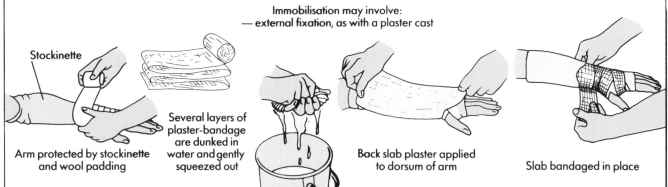

Stockinette

Arm protected by stockinette and wool padding

Several layers of plaster-bandage are dunked in water and gently squeezed out

Back slab plaster applied to dorsum of arm

Slab bandaged in place

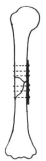

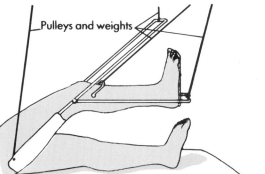

Pulleys and weights

— internal fixation: the ends of bone are held together with screws with or without a plate through the cortex, or a nail or screw running through the medullary cavity.

Traction is sometimes used to pull the bones into a good position for healing when otherwise the pull of muscles would produce distortion.

Rehabilitation aims to enable the fracture patient to return to his or her previous activity pattern.

When things go wrong — complications of healing

Malunion — the fracture heals crooked, so the bone cannot work properly. The bone has to be broken (osteotomy) and reset.

Delayed union or non-union — the ends are slow to unite or do not join at all; this is especially likely to happen when the blood supply is poor. It is treated by bone-grafting.

Damage to other tissues, such as muscles, tendons or nerves.
Blood vessel damage may produce ischaemic contracture of muscles, when they are replaced by non-contractile fibrous tissue. It is sometimes necessary to repair soft tissues surgically to get the best functional result.

JOINTS

A joint or articulation is the structure where two or more bones of the skeleton meet and may move on each other.
Long bones articulate at their ends, flat bones at their edges. The function of the joints is to allow movement.
This then makes possible both basic functions like respiration, and also limb movements
for manipulation of objects and motion from place to place.

Joints where little or no movement is possible

fibrous joints   cartilaginous joints

Fibrous joints, when the bones concerned are joined by fibrous tissue. This group includes sutures, gomphoses and syndesmoses.

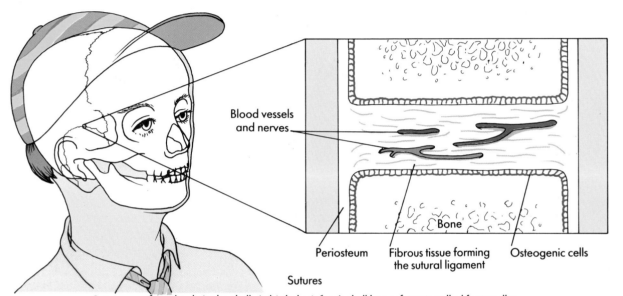

Blood vessels and nerves

Bone

Periosteum   Fibrous tissue forming   Osteogenic cells
                    the sutural ligament

Sutures

Sutures are found only in the skull. At birth the infant's skull has soft spots called fontanelles.
This means that during birth the bones can move and slide over each other, while still protecting the brain from damage.
The fontanelles close and disappear during early childhood, and during childhood and adolescence the skull can expand
by laying down new bone at the sutures. This allows space for the very important growth and development of the brain.

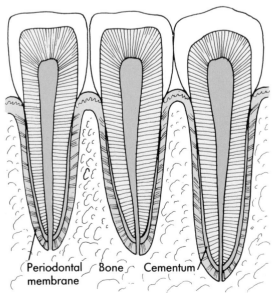

Periodontal   Bone   Cementum
membrane

Gomphoses are fixed peg-and-socket joints. The roots of the
teeth embedded in the jawbone are examples.

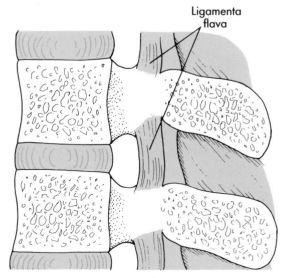

Ligamenta flava

Syndesmoses are joints where the bones are connected by
ligaments which permit a little movement. They are found between
the tibia and fibula, the radius and ulna and the vertebrae
(ligamenta flava).

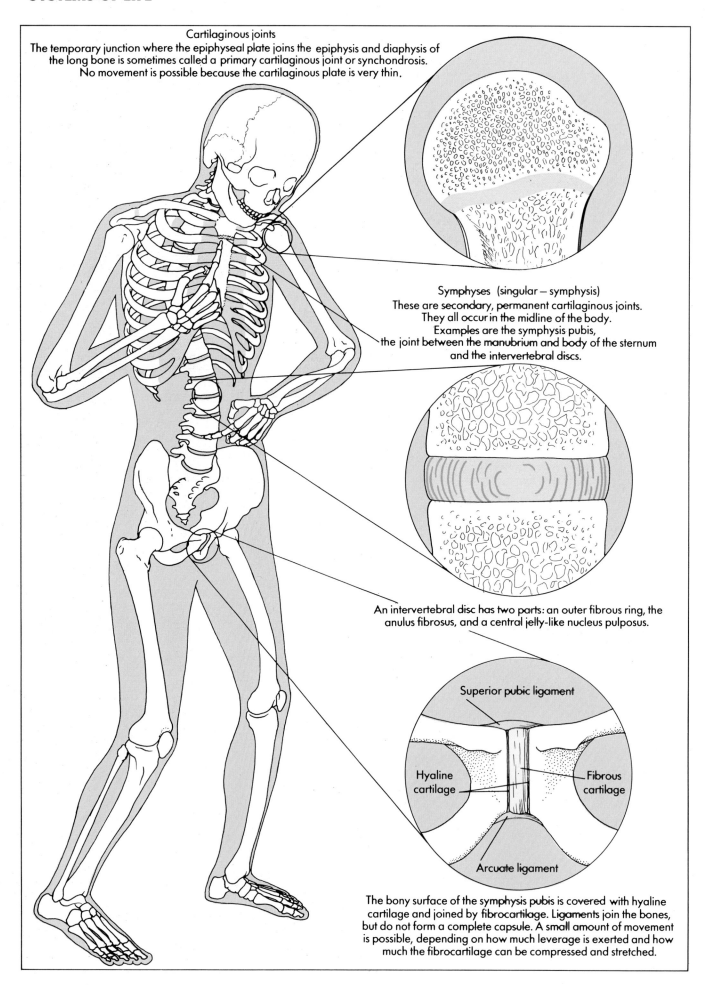

Cartilaginous joints
The temporary junction where the epiphyseal plate joins the epiphysis and diaphysis of the long bone is sometimes called a primary cartilaginous joint or synchondrosis. No movement is possible because the cartilaginous plate is very thin.

Symphyses (singular – symphysis)
These are secondary, permanent cartilaginous joints.
They all occur in the midline of the body.
Examples are the symphysis pubis,
the joint between the manubrium and body of the sternum
and the intervertebral discs.

An intervertebral disc has two parts: an outer fibrous ring, the anulus fibrosus, and a central jelly-like nucleus pulposus.

Superior pubic ligament

Hyaline cartilage

Fibrous cartilage

Arcuate ligament

The bony surface of the symphysis pubis is covered with hyaline cartilage and joined by fibrocartilage. Ligaments join the bones, but do not form a complete capsule. A small amount of movement is possible, depending on how much leverage is exerted and how much the fibrocartilage can be compressed and stretched.

Synovial joints
All joints that move to an appreciable extent are synovial joints.
Some, such as the shoulder joint, are very mobile; others, like those between the bases of the metacarpal bones, move only a little.

Shoulder joint (diagrammatic)

Synovial membrane

Articular surfaces of the bones, covered with smooth, shiny hyaline cartilage.

Joint cavity containing synovial fluid. This lubricates joint movement and may also carry nutrients to the cartilage, which has no blood vessels of its own.

Fibrous capsule enclosing the whole joint. It is lined throughout by synovial membrane, except over the articular cartilage.

Biceps tendon

Ligaments connecting the bones. They are usually, but not always, outside the joint. Ligaments are flexible enough to allow normal movement, but too tough and unyielding to permit abnormal movement unless a damagingly strong force is applied.

Cruciate ligaments

Articular discs called menisci subdivide some joints. They are joined to the inside of the capsule and increase the range of movement of the joint.

Knee joint (diagrammatic)

Arteries and veins form net-like plexuses round the joint.
The branches pierce the synovial membrane and anastomose over it, ending at the edge of the hyaline cartilage.
Lymphatics drain along the vessels to the regional nodes.

Joints are usually innervated by the nerves supplying the muscles that act on them.
This helps the joints to keep stable at rest and to move in a controlled way.

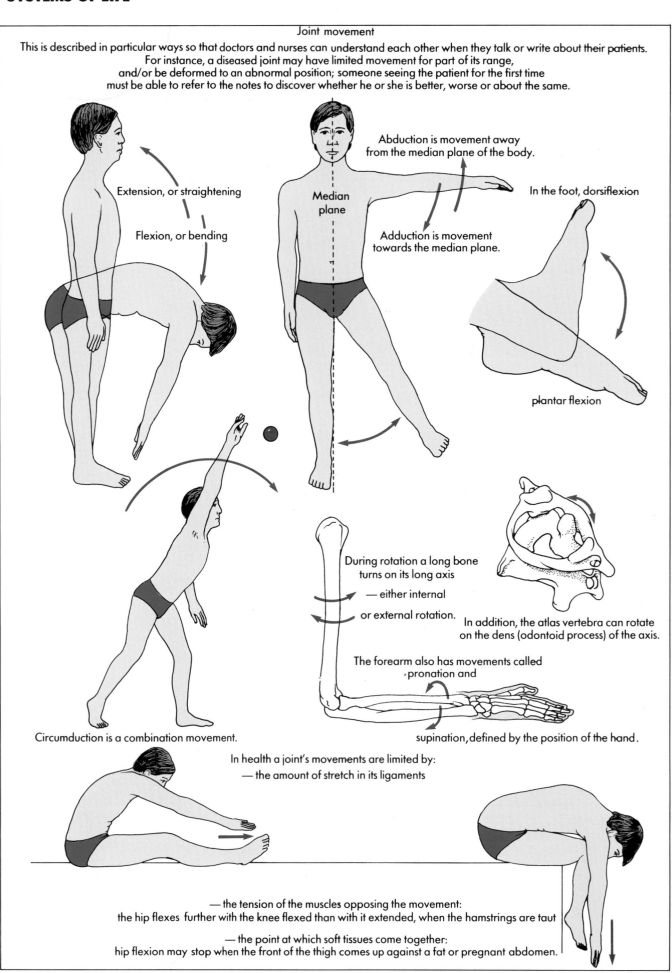

Joint movement

This is described in particular ways so that doctors and nurses can understand each other when they talk or write about their patients.
For instance, a diseased joint may have limited movement for part of its range,
and/or be deformed to an abnormal position; someone seeing the patient for the first time
must be able to refer to the notes to discover whether he or she is better, worse or about the same.

Extension, or straightening

Flexion, or bending

Median plane

Abduction is movement away
from the median plane of the body.

Adduction is movement
towards the median plane.

In the foot, dorsiflexion

plantar flexion

During rotation a long bone
turns on its long axis

— either internal

or external rotation.

In addition, the atlas vertebra can rotate
on the dens (odontoid process) of the axis.

The forearm also has movements called
pronation and

Circumduction is a combination movement.

supination, defined by the position of the hand.

In health a joint's movements are limited by:
— the amount of stretch in its ligaments

— the tension of the muscles opposing the movement:
the hip flexes further with the knee flexed than with it extended, when the hamstrings are taut

— the point at which soft tissues come together:
hip flexion may stop when the front of the thigh comes up against a fat or pregnant abdomen.

Joints of the upper limb
The upper limbs of a human are adapted for mobility and free movement.
This allows humans to perform a great variety of simple and complex tasks with their arms and hands.

The shoulder joint
This has a wider range of movement than any other joint in the body.
However, such mobility can only be achieved at the price of some instability and weakness, so dislocation of the shoulder is common.

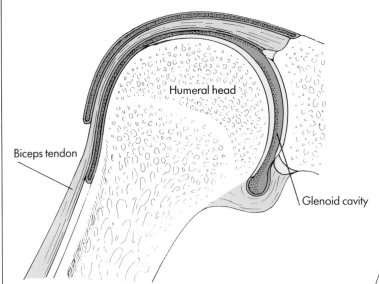

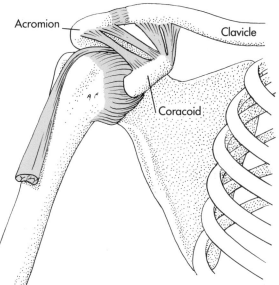

Ball-and-socket joint between the head of the humerus,
which is half a sphere, and the small and shallow glenoid cavity.
Only a small part of the humeral head
can be in contact with the glenoid cavity at any one time.

The main supports of the joint are the strong muscles
and tendons around it, forming the rotator cuff.

Above, it is protected by the arch formed by the two
prongs of the scapula, the acromion
and the coracoid, and by the ligament between them.

Arm movements are helped by rotation of the scapula
on the chest wall.

The elbow joint
(humerus with ulna and humerus with radius)

This is a hinge joint, with movements of flexion
and extension in one plane.

Pivot joint between head of radius and ring
formed by the radial notch of the ulna
and the anular ligament.

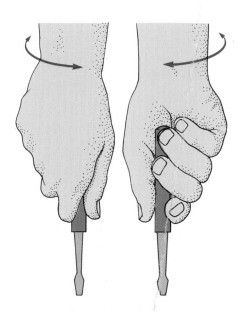

Pivot joint between the head of the ulna
and the ulnar notch of the lower end of the radius.

The radius and ulna move on each other
at the upper and lower ends to twist into
pronation and supination.

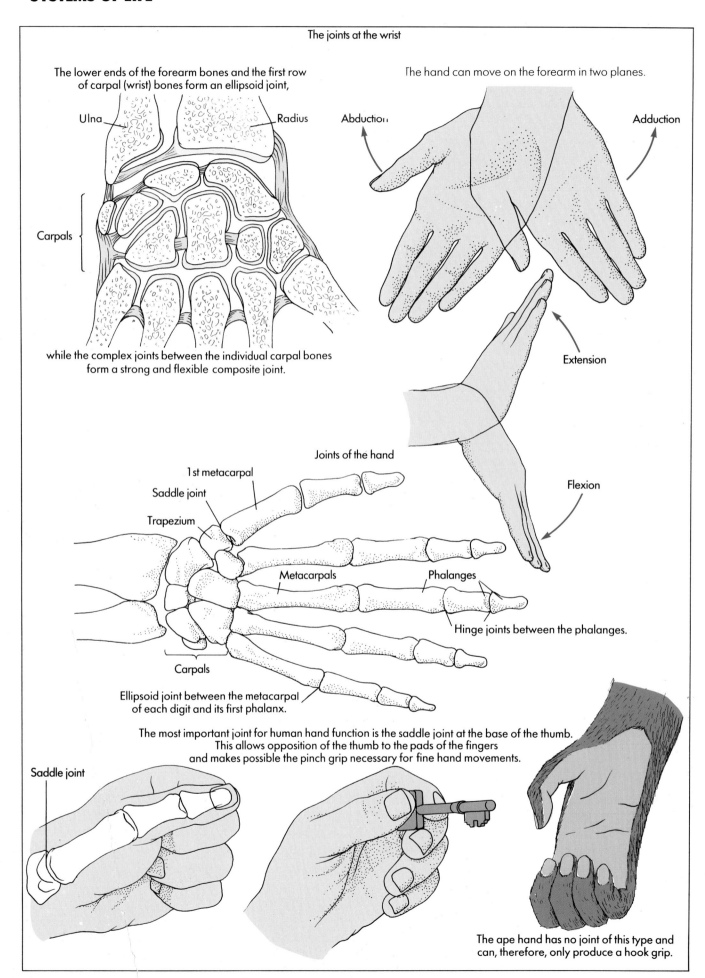

The joints at the wrist

The lower ends of the forearm bones and the first row of carpal (wrist) bones form an ellipsoid joint,

Ulna

Radius

Carpals

while the complex joints between the individual carpal bones form a strong and flexible composite joint.

The hand can move on the forearm in two planes.

Abduction

Adduction

Extension

Flexion

Joints of the hand

1st metacarpal

Saddle joint

Trapezium

Metacarpals

Phalanges

Hinge joints between the phalanges.

Carpals

Ellipsoid joint between the metacarpal of each digit and its first phalanx.

The most important joint for human hand function is the saddle joint at the base of the thumb. This allows opposition of the thumb to the pads of the fingers and makes possible the pinch grip necessary for fine hand movements.

Saddle joint

The ape hand has no joint of this type and can, therefore, only produce a hook grip.

Joints of the lower limb
The lower limb with its thicker, stronger bones is adapted for weight-bearing.

The hip joint
This is a ball-and-socket joint, with mobility to some extent sacrificed to stability;
if the joint were as mobile as the shoulder, it would be very likely to dislocate in weight-bearing.

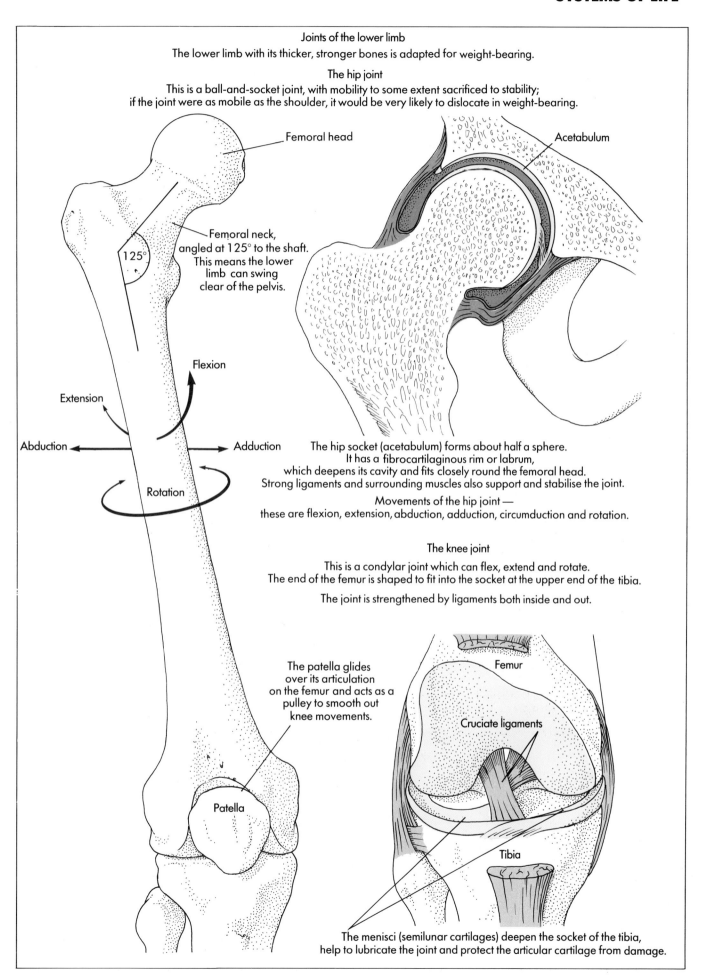

Femoral head

Acetabulum

Femoral neck, angled at 125° to the shaft. This means the lower limb can swing clear of the pelvis.

125°

Flexion

Extension

Abduction

Adduction

Rotation

The hip socket (acetabulum) forms about half a sphere.
It has a fibrocartilaginous rim or labrum,
which deepens its cavity and fits closely round the femoral head.
Strong ligaments and surrounding muscles also support and stabilise the joint.

Movements of the hip joint —
these are flexion, extension, abduction, adduction, circumduction and rotation.

The knee joint
This is a condylar joint which can flex, extend and rotate.
The end of the femur is shaped to fit into the socket at the upper end of the tibia.

The joint is strengthened by ligaments both inside and out.

The patella glides over its articulation on the femur and acts as a pulley to smooth out knee movements.

Patella

Femur

Cruciate ligaments

Tibia

The menisci (semilunar cartilages) deepen the socket of the tibia,
help to lubricate the joint and protect the articular cartilage from damage.

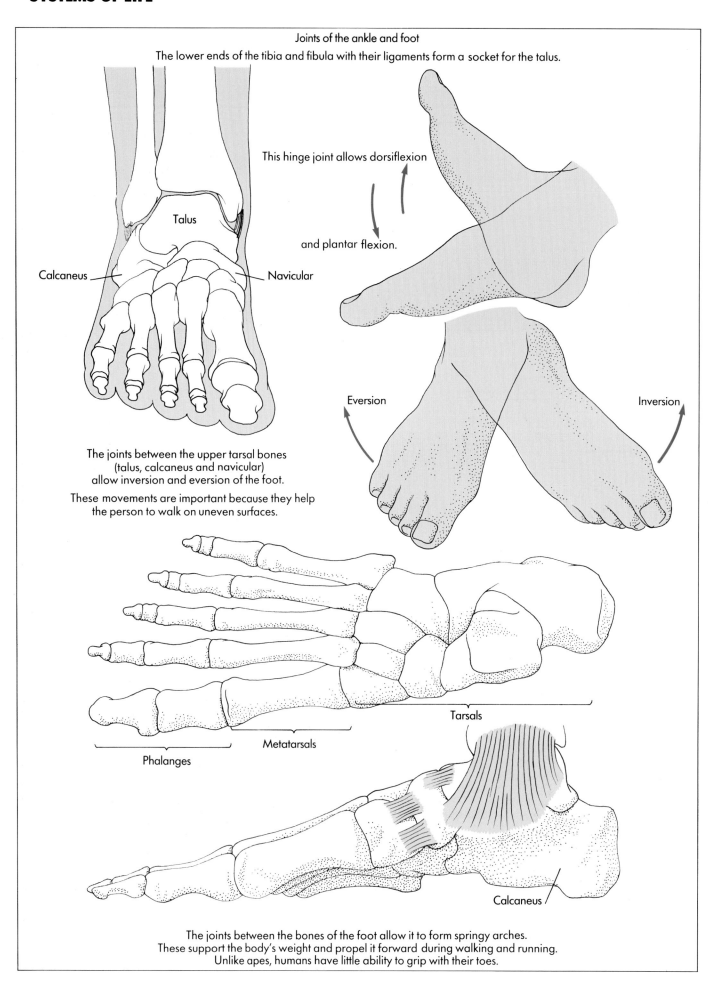

Joints of the ankle and foot
The lower ends of the tibia and fibula with their ligaments form a socket for the talus.

Talus

Calcaneus

Navicular

This hinge joint allows dorsiflexion

and plantar flexion.

Eversion

Inversion

The joints between the upper tarsal bones
(talus, calcaneus and navicular)
allow inversion and eversion of the foot.

These movements are important because they help
the person to walk on uneven surfaces.

Tarsals

Metatarsals

Phalanges

Calcaneus

The joints between the bones of the foot allow it to form springy arches.
These support the body's weight and propel it forward during walking and running.
Unlike apes, humans have little ability to grip with their toes.

MUSCLE

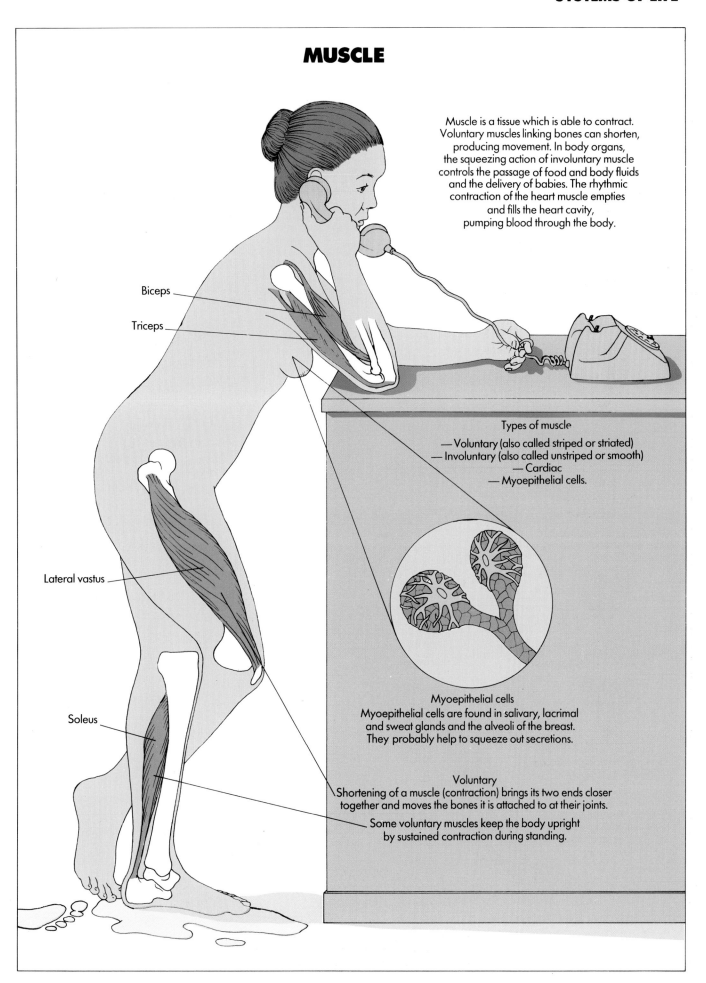

Muscle is a tissue which is able to contract. Voluntary muscles linking bones can shorten, producing movement. In body organs, the squeezing action of involuntary muscle controls the passage of food and body fluids and the delivery of babies. The rhythmic contraction of the heart muscle empties and fills the heart cavity, pumping blood through the body.

Biceps

Triceps

Lateral vastus

Soleus

Types of muscle

— Voluntary (also called striped or striated)
— Involuntary (also called unstriped or smooth)
— Cardiac
— Myoepithelial cells.

Myoepithelial cells
Myoepithelial cells are found in salivary, lacrimal and sweat glands and the alveoli of the breast. They probably help to squeeze out secretions.

Voluntary
Shortening of a muscle (contraction) brings its two ends closer together and moves the bones it is attached to at their joints.

Some voluntary muscles keep the body upright by sustained contraction during standing.

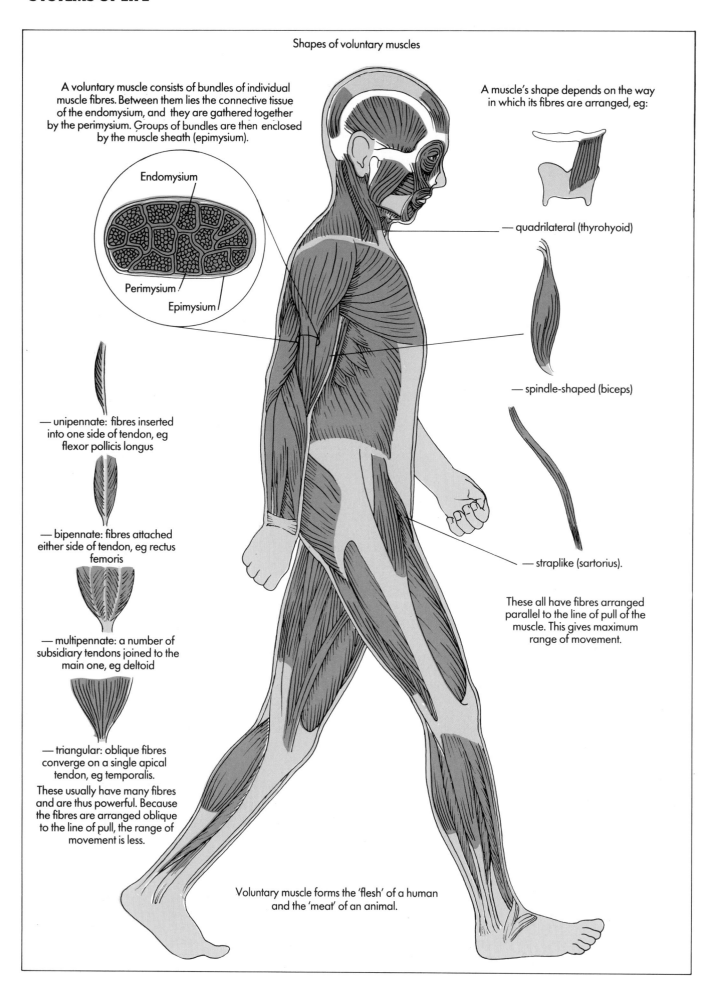

Shapes of voluntary muscles

A voluntary muscle consists of bundles of individual muscle fibres. Between them lies the connective tissue of the endomysium, and they are gathered together by the perimysium. Groups of bundles are then enclosed by the muscle sheath (epimysium).

Endomysium

Perimysium

Epimysium

A muscle's shape depends on the way in which its fibres are arranged, eg:

— quadrilateral (thyrohyoid)

— spindle-shaped (biceps)

— straplike (sartorius).

These all have fibres arranged parallel to the line of pull of the muscle. This gives maximum range of movement.

— unipennate: fibres inserted into one side of tendon, eg flexor pollicis longus

— bipennate: fibres attached either side of tendon, eg rectus femoris

— multipennate: a number of subsidiary tendons joined to the main one, eg deltoid

— triangular: oblique fibres converge on a single apical tendon, eg temporalis.

These usually have many fibres and are thus powerful. Because the fibres are arranged oblique to the line of pull, the range of movement is less.

Voluntary muscle forms the 'flesh' of a human and the 'meat' of an animal.

Muscles can join:
— bones, directly when perimysium joins periosteum
— skin, directly, lying flat against it and blending with subcutaneous tissues.
Most muscles end in either a flat, sheet-like aponeurosis or a cord-like tendon (sometimes called 'sinew' or 'leader'). Tendons consist of strong white collagen fibres that do not stretch. The fibres are bound together by interfascicular tissue containing vessels and nerves. This thickens to ensheath the fibres as epitendineum or peritendineum. The tissues of muscle and tendon blend into each other as they join. When tendon meets bone, its interfascicular tissue fuses with the periosteum, while the collagen fibres pass through into the cortical bone.

Tendon helpers — retinacula and sheaths
Beneath the skin lie the fatty superficial fascia and the dense and inelastic deep fascia. This binds down and covers muscles and also forms septa between them. Thickened bands of deep fascia cross tendons as retinacula, attached to bone on either side to form tunnels. They prevent the tendons from 'bowstringing' away from the bones as their muscles contract, and they also serve as pulleys.

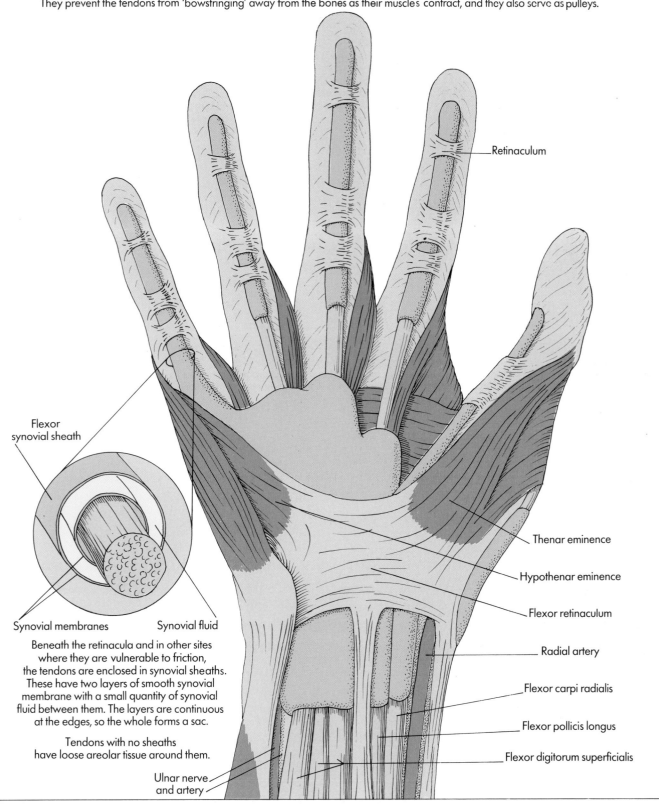

Retinaculum

Flexor synovial sheath

Synovial membranes   Synovial fluid

Beneath the retinacula and in other sites where they are vulnerable to friction, the tendons are enclosed in synovial sheaths. These have two layers of smooth synovial membrane with a small quantity of synovial fluid between them. The layers are continuous at the edges, so the whole forms a sac.

Tendons with no sheaths have loose areolar tissue around them.

Thenar eminence

Hypothenar eminence

Flexor retinaculum

Radial artery

Flexor carpi radialis

Flexor pollicis longus

Flexor digitorum superficialis

Ulnar nerve and artery

Organisation of movement (simplified)

The brain does not control muscles as separate units but in patterns corresponding to particular movements.
In health this is carefully co-ordinated so that each muscle involved in a movement
contracts by precisely the right amount at exactly the right point in the sequence.

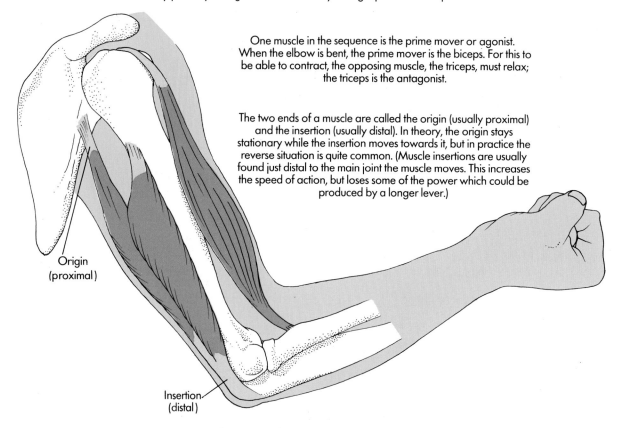

One muscle in the sequence is the prime mover or agonist.
When the elbow is bent, the prime mover is the biceps. For this to
be able to contract, the opposing muscle, the triceps, must relax;
the triceps is the antagonist.

The two ends of a muscle are called the origin (usually proximal)
and the insertion (usually distal). In theory, the origin stays
stationary while the insertion moves towards it, but in practice the
reverse situation is quite common. (Muscle insertions are usually
found just distal to the main joint the muscle moves. This increases
the speed of action, but loses some of the power which could be
produced by a longer lever.)

Origin
(proximal)

Insertion
(distal)

During movement, fixation muscles may contract to keep the origin still:
when the deltoid abducts the arm, the clavicle and scapula are steadied by fixation muscles.
Synergists may also contract to prevent wasteful movement of intervening joints.

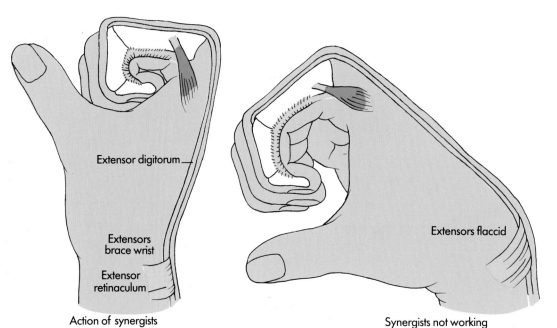

Extensor digitorum

Extensors
brace wrist

Extensor
retinaculum

Extensors flaccid

Action of synergists

If the wrist extensors contract with the long flexors of the fingers,
there is no waste of power as the tendons cross the wrist joint,
and the fingers curl tightly.

Synergists not working

When the wrist extensors do not brace the wrist, it flexes too,
and the fingers can only flex loosely.

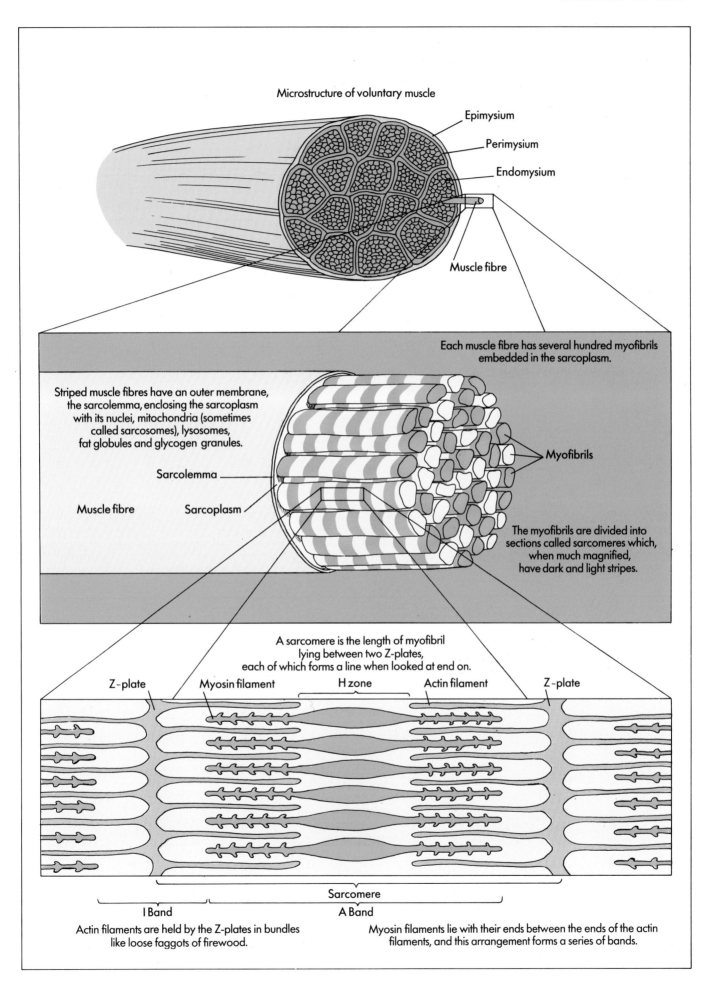

Microstructure of voluntary muscle

Epimysium

Perimysium

Endomysium

Muscle fibre

Each muscle fibre has several hundred myofibrils embedded in the sarcoplasm.

Striped muscle fibres have an outer membrane, the sarcolemma, enclosing the sarcoplasm with its nuclei, mitochondria (sometimes called sarcosomes), lysosomes, fat globules and glycogen granules.

Myofibrils

Sarcolemma

Muscle fibre   Sarcoplasm

The myofibrils are divided into sections called sarcomeres which, when much magnified, have dark and light stripes.

A sarcomere is the length of myofibril lying between two Z-plates, each of which forms a line when looked at end on.

Z-plate   Myosin filament   H zone   Actin filament   Z-plate

Sarcomere

I Band   A Band

Actin filaments are held by the Z-plates in bundles like loose faggots of firewood.

Myosin filaments lie with their ends between the ends of the actin filaments, and this arrangement forms a series of bands.

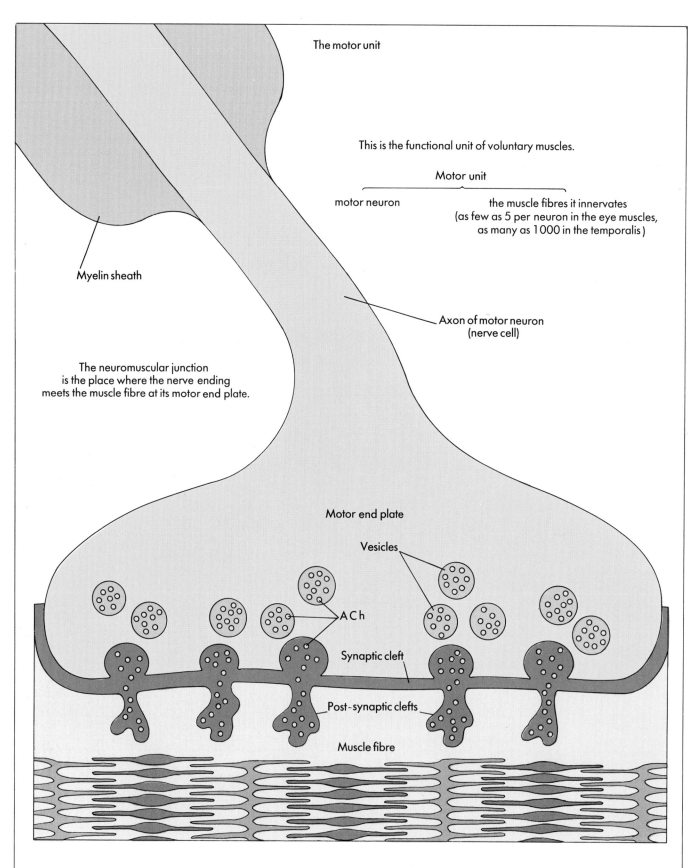

The motor unit

This is the functional unit of voluntary muscles.

Motor unit

motor neuron · · · · · · · · the muscle fibres it innervates
(as few as 5 per neuron in the eye muscles,
as many as 1000 in the temporalis)

Myelin sheath

Axon of motor neuron
(nerve cell)

The neuromuscular junction
is the place where the nerve ending
meets the muscle fibre at its motor end plate.

Motor end plate

Vesicles

ACh

Synaptic cleft

Post-synaptic clefts

Muscle fibre

When the nerve fires, vesicles in it empty the transmitter substance acetylcholine (ACh)
into the synaptic cleft between nerve and muscle.
The acetylcholine then reacts with receptors in the post-synaptic clefts of the muscle membrane.
This produces an electric current called an action potential in the muscle fibre, which makes it contract.
After firing, the acetylcholine is rapidly destroyed by enzymes called cholinesterases;
until the old acetylcholine is removed, the muscle fibre cannot fire again.

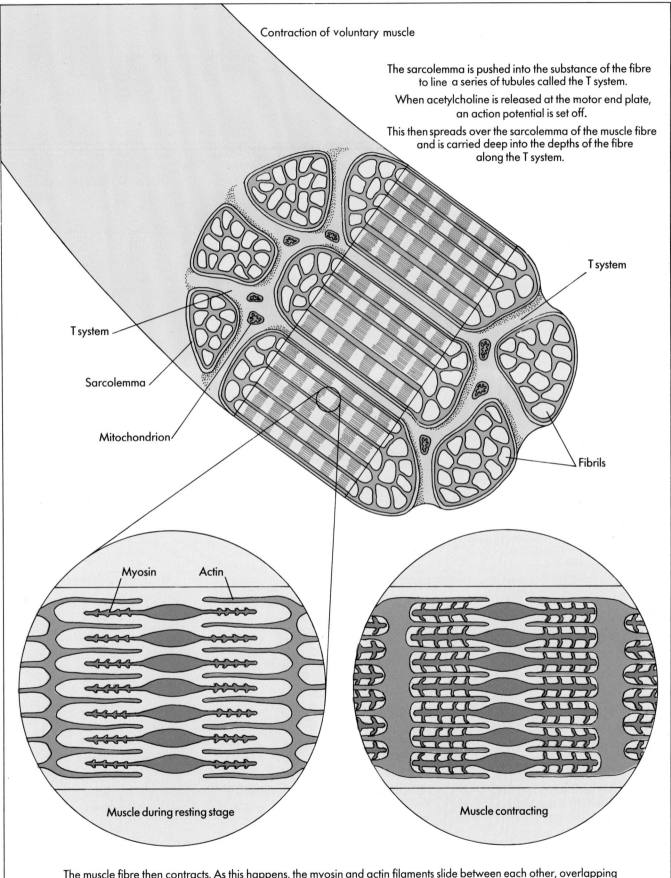

Contraction of voluntary muscle

The sarcolemma is pushed into the substance of the fibre to line a series of tubules called the T system.

When acetylcholine is released at the motor end plate, an action potential is set off.

This then spreads over the sarcolemma of the muscle fibre and is carried deep into the depths of the fibre along the T system.

T system

T system

Sarcolemma

Mitochondrion

Fibrils

Myosin   Actin

Muscle during resting stage

Muscle contracting

The muscle fibre then contracts. As this happens, the myosin and actin filaments slide between each other, overlapping more and more as the Z-plates move closer together. The filaments themselves do not change in length, and the process has to stop when the ends of the myosin filaments have slid so far into the actin bundles that their ends are against the Z-plates. By this time the actin filament ends overlap each other at the centre of the sarcomere.

How it happens

In the resting, unpolarised state the actin and myosin filaments are free to slide loosely past each other;
this allows antagonists to relax when the opposing muscles contract.

Contraction

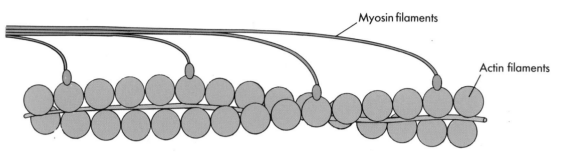

Myosin filaments

Actin filaments

The bulbous heads of the myosin filaments become attached to the actin filaments.

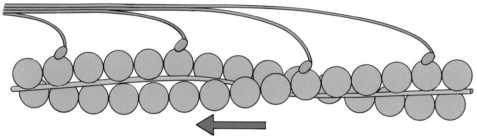

The head of each myosin filament then flexes on its neck, pulling the actin filament along.

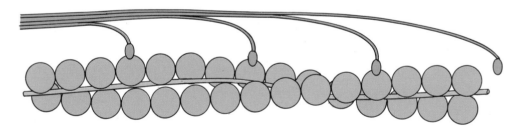

The myosin heads then uncouple, re-extend and reattach further along the actin filament.
Again the myosin heads flex on their necks, and again pull the filament along.
This process happens at both ends of the myosin filament, with the pull in opposite directions.
The two sets of filaments overlap increasingly on either side of the Z-line, and the whole sarcomere shortens.

Muscle also contains elastic components arranged in parallel with the sarcomeres.
These act as 'stops' to extension, so the interlocking filaments cannot be pulled so far apart that they dislocate.

The force of contraction of a muscle depends on:
— how many motor units are activated
— the frequency of the action potentials;
if they keep coming the filaments will repeat their sliding process until the end position is reached.

Body changes during exercise
These aim to deliver more oxygen-rich blood to the working muscles, and to dispose of the waste carbon dioxide and lactate.

1. The heart.
The heart pumps more blood per minute as it beats faster and the ventricles contract more powerfully, emptying their contents more completely; this happens because of stimuli from the sympathetic nerves.

2. Respiration.
Lung ventilation increases enormously, so more oxygen is available. Also, more oxygen is given off by the circulating haemoglobin.

3. Blood flow.
Muscle blood vessels dilate because of the direct effects of an increase in carbon dioxide and lactate and a fall in the amount of oxygen. (This outweighs the slight hindrance of pressure from contracting muscles.) Increased skin blood flow aims to disperse heat, and the heart's blood supply increases to cope with its extra workload.

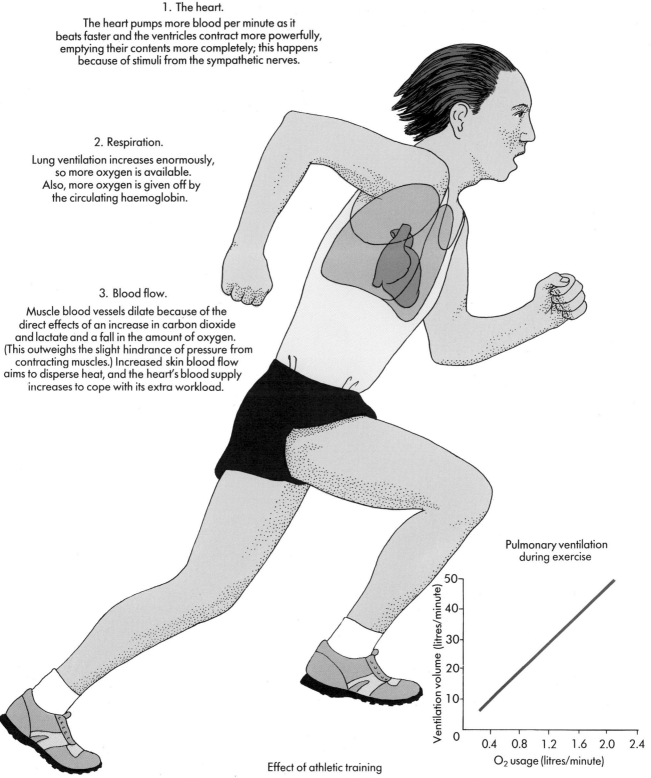

Pulmonary ventilation during exercise

Ventilation volume (litres/minute)

50
40
30
20
10
0

0.4 0.8 1.2 1.6 2.0 2.4

O_2 usage (litres/minute)

Effect of athletic training
A trained athlete has a greater muscle mass and also more muscle mitochondria; these give a greater ability to break down glucose aerobically, so it takes longer to develop lactic acidosis in muscles.

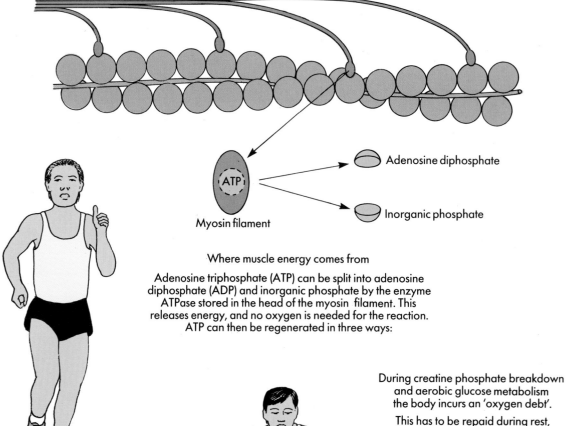

Myosin filament

Adenosine diphosphate

Inorganic phosphate

Where muscle energy comes from

Adenosine triphosphate (ATP) can be split into adenosine diphosphate (ADP) and inorganic phosphate by the enzyme ATPase stored in the head of the myosin filament. This releases energy, and no oxygen is needed for the reaction. ATP can then be regenerated in three ways:

During creatine phosphate breakdown and aerobic glucose metabolism the body incurs an 'oxygen debt'.

This has to be repaid during rest, so CrP and glycogen reserves can be replaced.

1. Breakdown of creatine phosphate (CrP).

CrP is stored in muscle and its energy is rapidly available. However, stores are small and are soon used up. Sufficient energy can be provided for a brief maximum effort like a 100-metre sprint.

2. Anaerobic breakdown of muscle glycogen.

Lactic acid accumulates, lowering pH; this restricts chemical reactions, so not enough ATP is regenerated to continue the energy supply. Muscle fatigue then sets in and the runner has to rest. This happens whenever he or she is using more oxygen than the body can supply and the tissues are forced to manage without.

3. Aerobic oxidation of glucose to carbon dioxide (CO_2).

This gives more energy than anaerobic metabolism, and is the only satisfactory method for continuous heavy exercise. Extra oxygen needs to be delivered for it to happen; if O_2 is in short supply glucose can be broken down anaerobically, but lactic acidosis occurs as with glycogen, and the exercise is then interrupted by the need to rest.

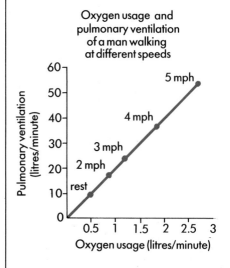

Oxygen usage and pulmonary ventilation of a man walking at different speeds

Pulmonary ventilation (litres/minute)

5 mph

4 mph

3 mph

2 mph

rest

Oxygen usage (litres/minute)

Cardiac muscle

Cardiac muscle is found only in the heart and the ends of the great vessels as they enter it.
It is able to contract rhythmically to maintain the circulation, and has atypical fibres that co-ordinate its activity.

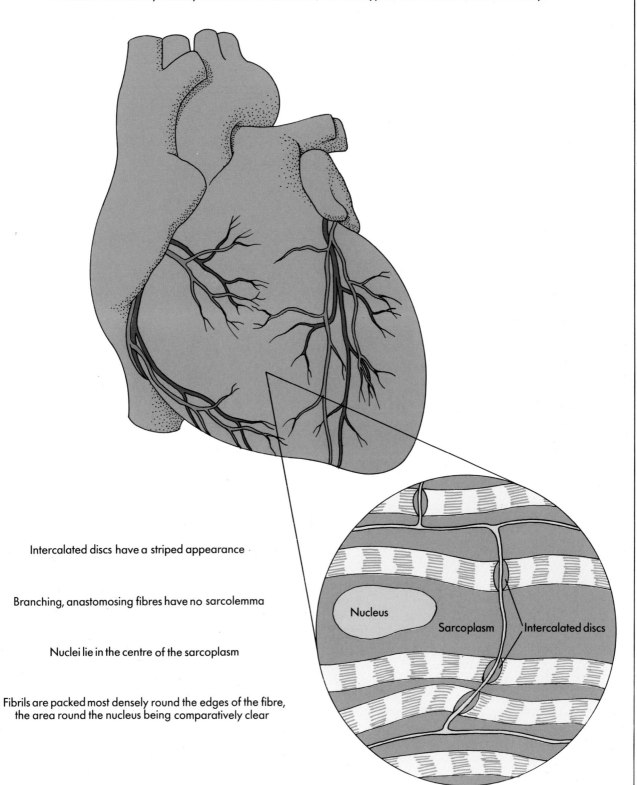

Intercalated discs have a striped appearance

Branching, anastomosing fibres have no sarcolemma

Nuclei lie in the centre of the sarcoplasm

Fibrils are packed most densely round the edges of the fibre,
the area round the nucleus being comparatively clear

There are two types of heart muscle fibres:

— fibres that respond to electrical impulses by contracting:
the heart muscle proper or myocardium

— fibres that start and then carry electrical impulses through
the heart muscle.

Cardiac muscle has an intrinsic ability to generate a contraction stimulus,
though in it the 'pacemaker' is localised and has a faster beat.
From the sinu-atrial (SA) node the impulse spreads through the atria to the atrioventricular (AV) node,
from where it spreads through the Purkinje system to the whole myocardium.

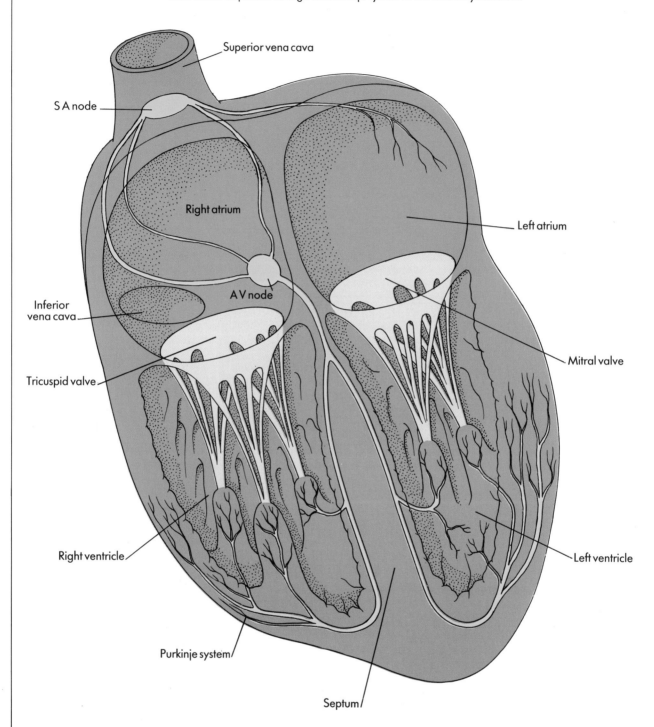

Control of contraction of cardiac muscles

Though the heart can beat autonomously, an intact nerve supply helps it to respond to the changing needs of its owner.
The autonomic nerves supplying the heart can alter its rate and force of contraction, and also affect its excitability and the speed
of conduction within it. Parasympathetic fibres carried in the vagus slow the heart, while sympathetic fibres make it beat faster.
Disturbances of blood chemistry, especially of potassium and calcium, also affect the heart muscle.

Smooth muscle

Smooth (involuntary) muscle is found in the gut, the respiratory tract, the genitourinary apparatus, in the ducts of glands and in the iris and ciliary body of the eye. In the skin it erects hairs and empties sweat glands.

Contraction of smooth muscle in blood vessel walls affects their tone and thus the vascular resistance.

As the alternative name suggests, contraction of smooth muscle cannot be produced voluntarily.

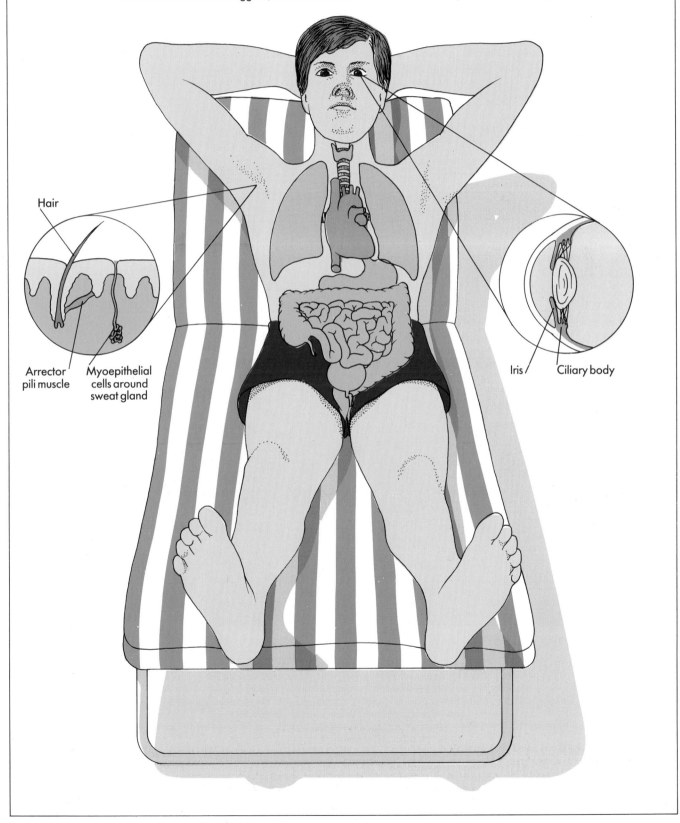

Hair

Arrector pili muscle

Myoepithelial cells around sweat gland

Iris

Ciliary body

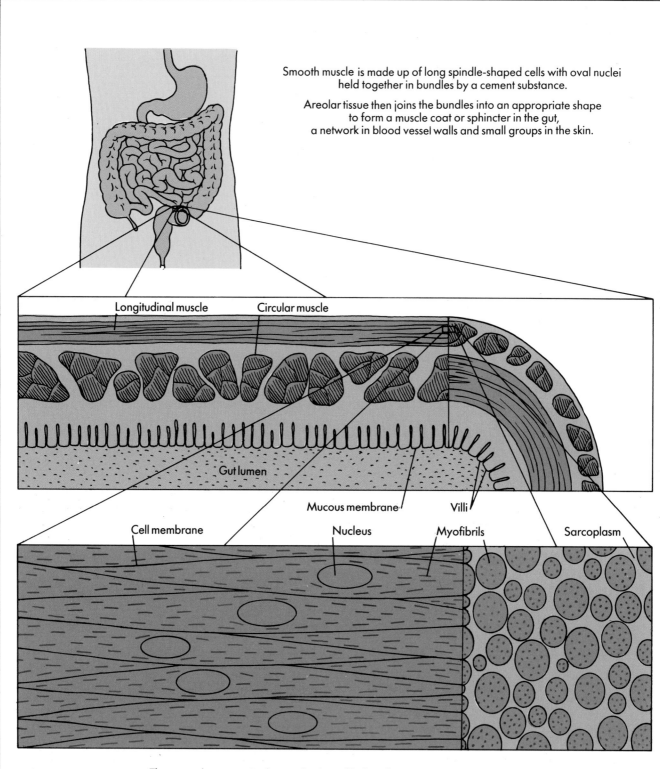

Smooth muscle is made up of long spindle-shaped cells with oval nuclei
held together in bundles by a cement substance.

Areolar tissue then joins the bundles into an appropriate shape
to form a muscle coat or sphincter in the gut,
a network in blood vessel walls and small groups in the skin.

Longitudinal muscle   Circular muscle

Gut lumen

Mucous membrane   Villi

Cell membrane   Nucleus   Myofibrils   Sarcoplasm

The sarcoplasm contains longitudinal myofibrils with no cross striations (stripes).
There is no sarcolemma, just a delicate cell membrane.
The cells are packed together with the tapering end of one against the thick part of the next,
and they are probably connected by myofibrils passing from one cell to another.
Collagenous and elastic fibres form cell sheaths, continuous with the surrounding connective tissue;
this helps to distribute the force of cell contraction.
Sometimes a wave of contraction passes over the cell, so part is contracted and part relaxed;
sometimes the cell contracts throughout its length.
The contraction is slow and sustained, independent of the will, and tone is maintained after the supplying nerves are cut.
Blood vessels and lymphatics run in the connective tissue between the bundles.
The autonomic nerve supply forms a plexus with terminal fibres running between cells to end on or in them.
The sensory fibres lie in the connective tissues between the bundles.

Action of smooth muscle

Cells contain actin filaments and a kind of myosin.
The muscle is always partly contracted (a state of 'tone')
because it is easily excited by regular spontaneous depolarisation spikes.
There are two functional types of smooth muscle:

1. Single unit smooth muscle.

The cells are connected together by bridges called gap junctions.
They also have an intrinsic pacemaker, causing them to depolarise spontaneously .
When this happens, the excitation spreads through the gap junctions
to all the connected cells, which then depolarise as a single unit.
The contraction is called myogenic tone;
it can persist for a long time, and stretching causes further contraction.
Much of the muscle in small blood vessels is of this type, helping to regulate blood flow.
It is found in other sites where myogenic tone is useful — the gut, urinary tract and uterus,
for instance. Single unit smooth muscle is largely independent of external nerve impulses.

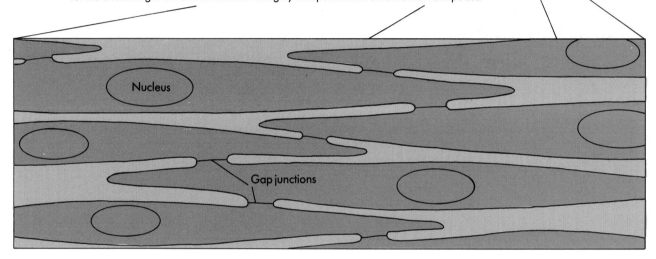

Contracted smooth muscle cell

Nucleus

Contractile bands containing
myosin and actin filaments

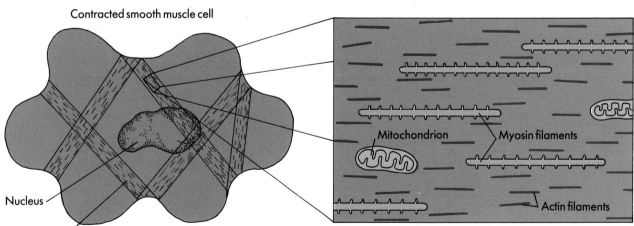

Mitochondrion

Myosin filaments

Actin filaments

2. Multi-unit smooth muscle.

In contrast, this type mostly contracts in response to autonomic nerve impulses, so-called neurogenic tone.
Gap junctions are rare, so the contraction may be localised to part of the muscle.
This type is found in the epididymis and vas, the iris and ciliary body and in some blood vessels.

Influences on smooth muscle include

— acetylcholine and noradrenaline from nerve endings

— hormones, eg the uterine muscle reacts to oestrogen, progesterone and oxytocin

— other substances, eg blood vessel muscle reacts to histamine, angiotensin II, vasopressin and many other agents.

Special features of smooth muscle

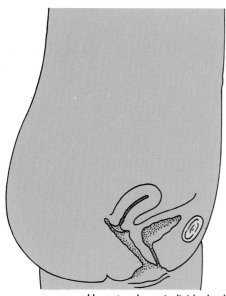 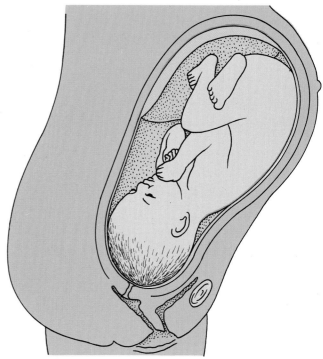

Hypertrophy — individual cells can grow enormously, as in the uterine wall during pregnancy.
People with raised blood pressure may have hypertrophied smooth muscle in their arterial walls.

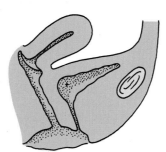 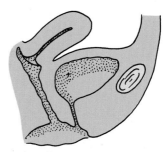

Plasticity — a stretched smooth muscle adjusts to a new length and relaxes its tension;
the muscle of the bladder wall expands without much increase in pressure until the bladder is almost full.

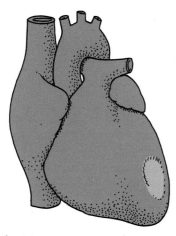 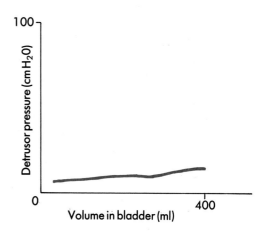

Repair after injury — scar tissue mostly forms,
as there is little cell division.

NERVOUS SYSTEM

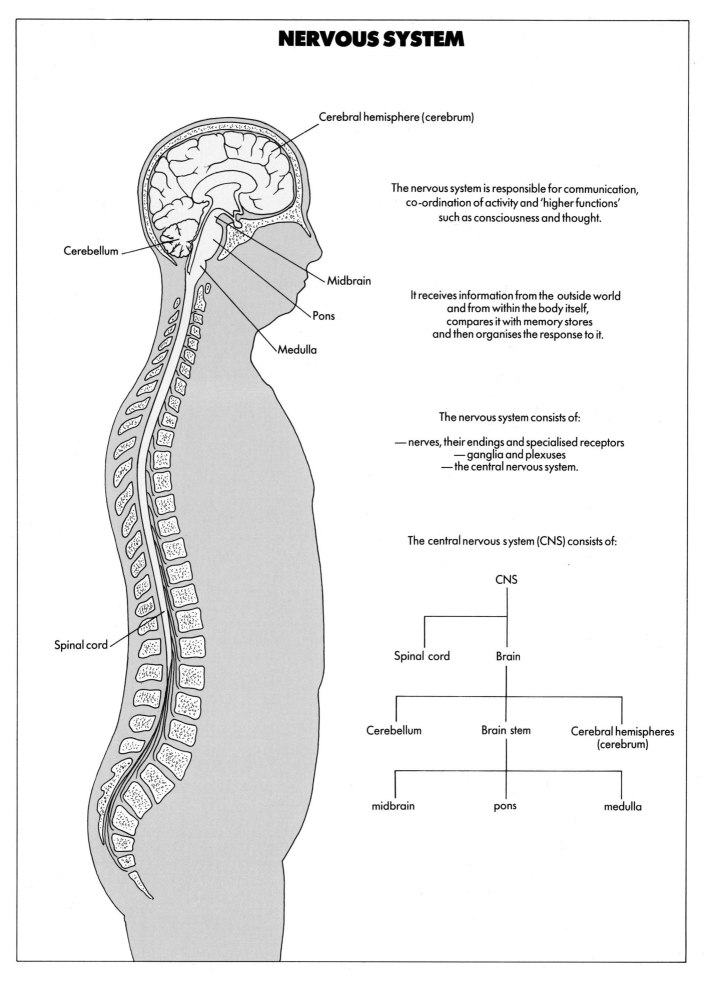

Cerebral hemisphere (cerebrum)

Cerebellum

Midbrain

Pons

Medulla

Spinal cord

The nervous system is responsible for communication, co-ordination of activity and 'higher functions' such as consciousness and thought.

It receives information from the outside world and from within the body itself, compares it with memory stores and then organises the response to it.

The nervous system consists of:

— nerves, their endings and specialised receptors
— ganglia and plexuses
— the central nervous system.

The central nervous system (CNS) consists of:

CNS

Spinal cord   Brain

Cerebellum   Brain stem   Cerebral hemispheres (cerebrum)

midbrain   pons   medulla

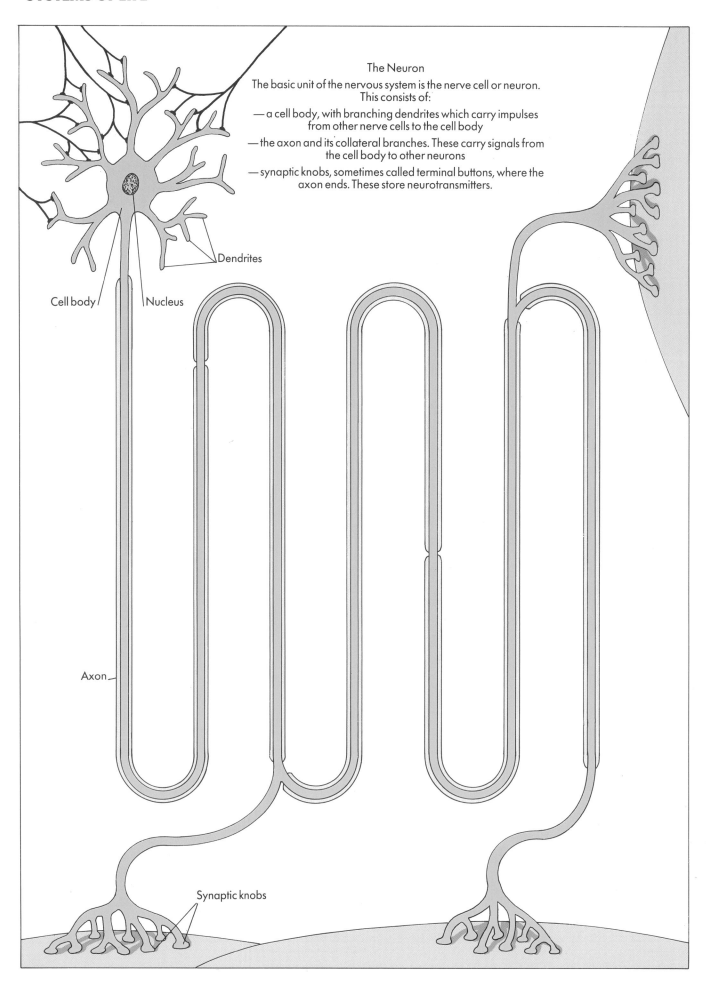

The Neuron
The basic unit of the nervous system is the nerve cell or neuron.
This consists of:

— a cell body, with branching dendrites which carry impulses
from other nerve cells to the cell body

— the axon and its collateral branches. These carry signals from
the cell body to other neurons

— synaptic knobs, sometimes called terminal buttons, where the
axon ends. These store neurotransmitters.

Dendrites

Cell body

Nucleus

Axon

Synaptic knobs

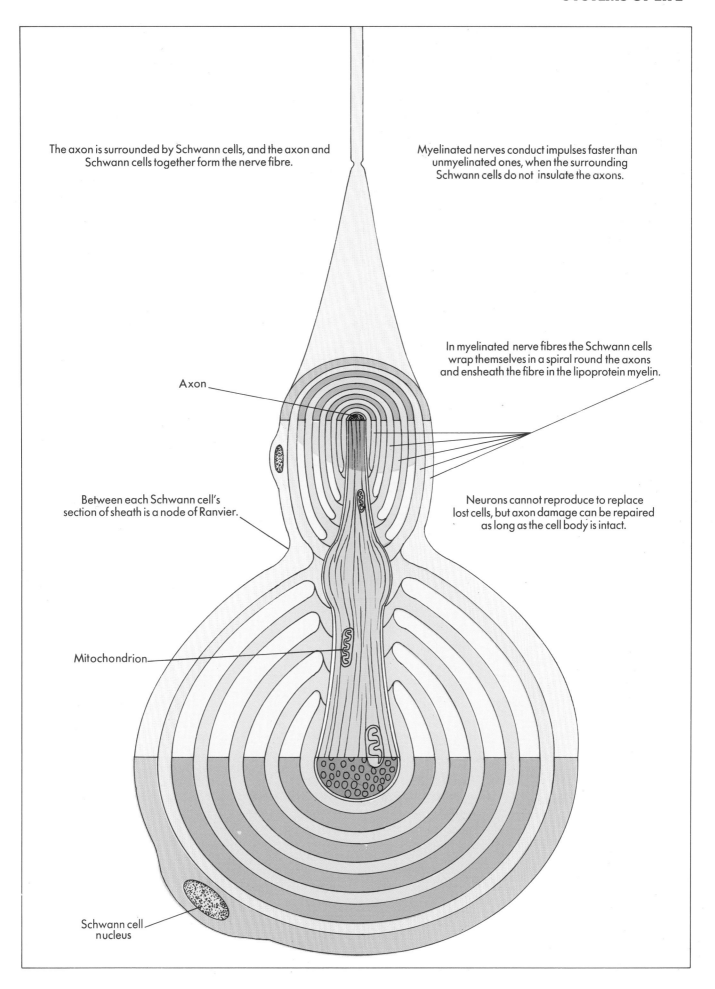

The axon is surrounded by Schwann cells, and the axon and Schwann cells together form the nerve fibre.

Myelinated nerves conduct impulses faster than unmyelinated ones, when the surrounding Schwann cells do not insulate the axons.

In myelinated nerve fibres the Schwann cells wrap themselves in a spiral round the axons and ensheath the fibre in the lipoprotein myelin.

Axon

Between each Schwann cell's section of sheath is a node of Ranvier.

Neurons cannot reproduce to replace lost cells, but axon damage can be repaired as long as the cell body is intact.

Mitochondrion

Schwann cell nucleus

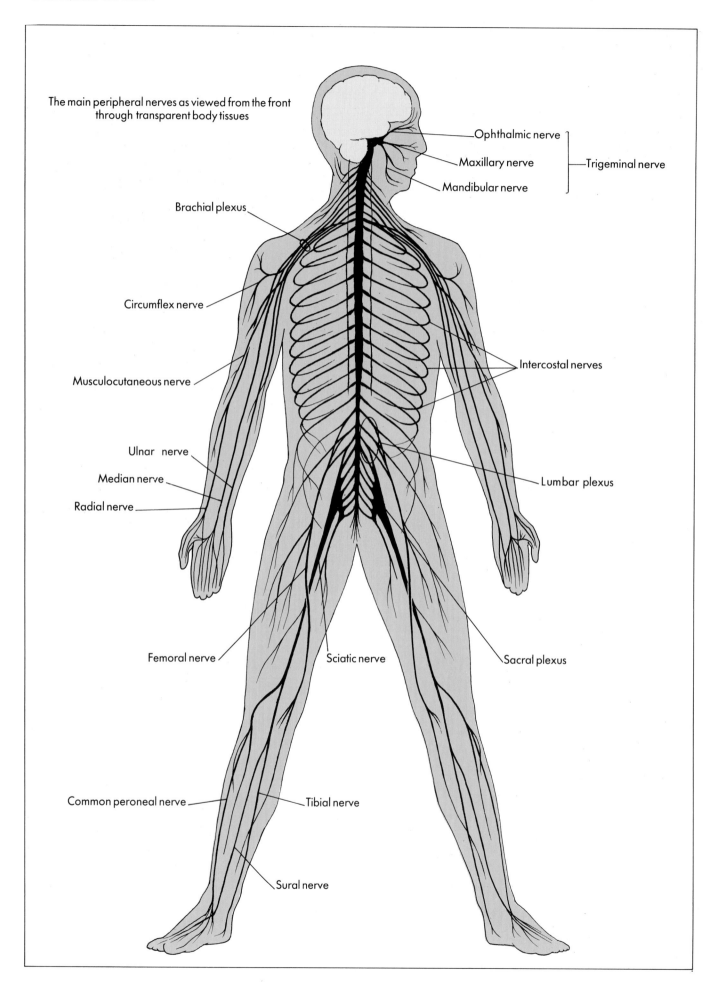

The main peripheral nerves as viewed from the front through transparent body tissues

Ophthalmic nerve ⎤
Maxillary nerve ⎬ Trigeminal nerve
Mandibular nerve ⎦

Brachial plexus

Circumflex nerve

Musculocutaneous nerve

Intercostal nerves

Ulnar nerve

Median nerve

Radial nerve

Lumbar plexus

Femoral nerve

Sciatic nerve

Sacral plexus

Common peroneal nerve

Tibial nerve

Sural nerve

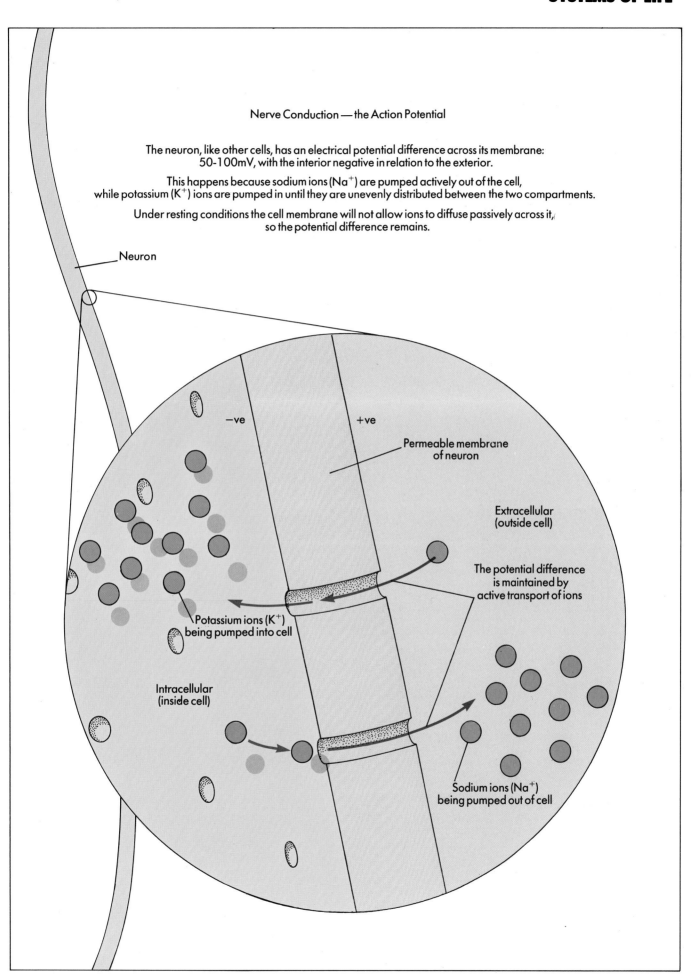

Nerve Conduction — the Action Potential

The neuron, like other cells, has an electrical potential difference across its membrane:
50-100mV, with the interior negative in relation to the exterior.

This happens because sodium ions (Na$^+$) are pumped actively out of the cell,
while potassium (K$^+$) ions are pumped in until they are unevenly distributed between the two compartments.

Under resting conditions the cell membrane will not allow ions to diffuse passively across it,
so the potential difference remains.

Neuron

−ve   +ve

Permeable membrane
of neuron

Extracellular
(outside cell)

The potential difference
is maintained by
active transport of ions

Potassium ions (K$^+$)
being pumped into cell

Intracellular
(inside cell)

Sodium ions (Na$^+$)
being pumped out of cell

Nerve cells are excitable – that is, they respond to stimuli.
These produce changes in the cell membrane's permeability to ions, and therefore change its electrical state:
the stimulus makes the cell permeable to sodium, which then rushes into it.
This is called depolarisation.

If the stimulus is big enough, the electrical change will make the nerve cell fire and the impulse will be conducted along its length.
This is an 'all or nothing' occurrence:
weak stimuli do not excite the cell, while any one that is above the threshold value is sufficient to make it fire.

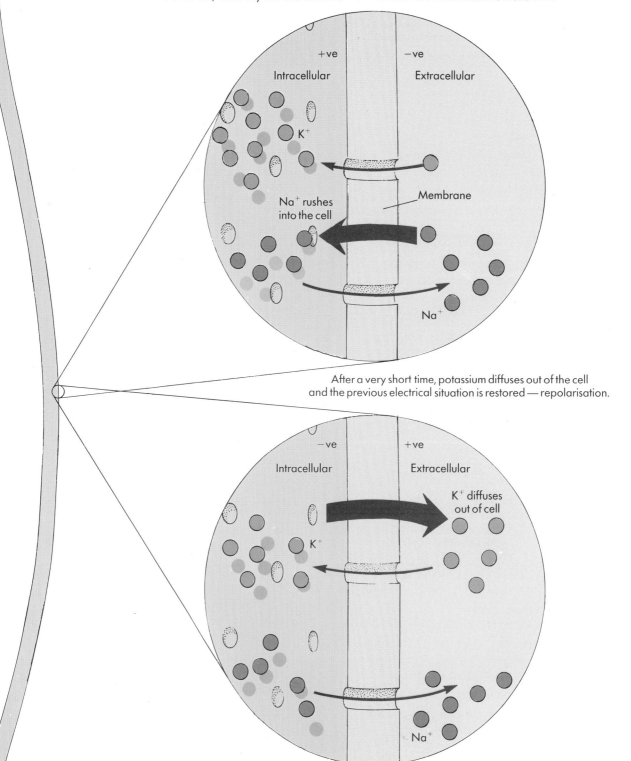

After a very short time, potassium diffuses out of the cell
and the previous electrical situation is restored — repolarisation.

For a short while after it fires, the nerve goes through a refractory period when it will not respond to a nerve stimulus.

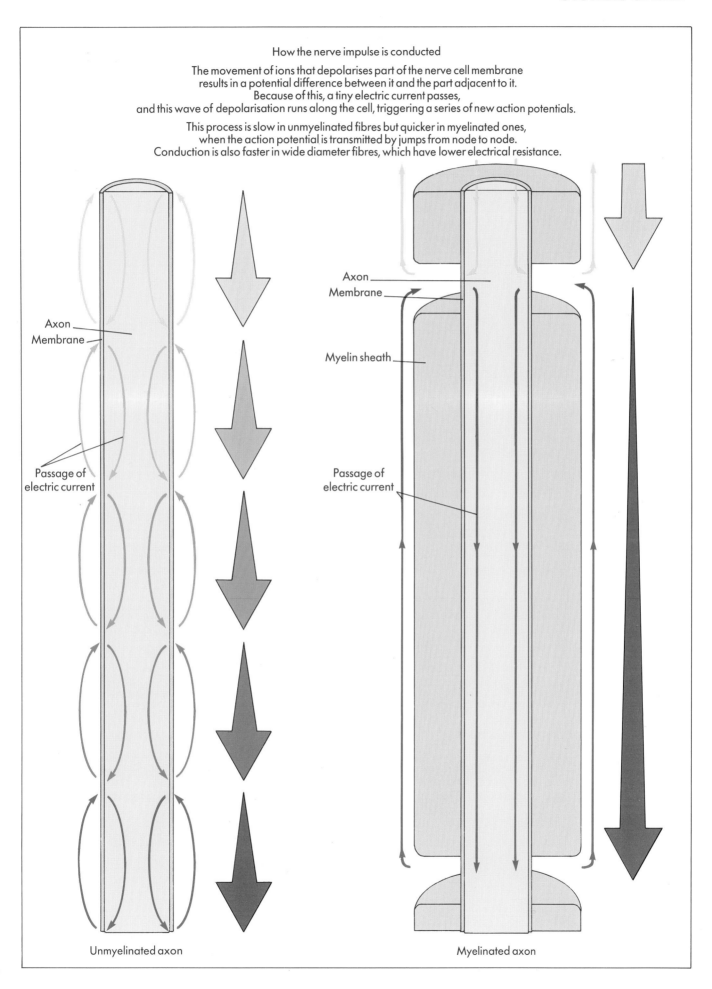

How the nerve impulse is conducted

The movement of ions that depolarises part of the nerve cell membrane
results in a potential difference between it and the part adjacent to it.
Because of this, a tiny electric current passes,
and this wave of depolarisation runs along the cell, triggering a series of new action potentials.

This process is slow in unmyelinated fibres but quicker in myelinated ones,
when the action potential is transmitted by jumps from node to node.
Conduction is also faster in wide diameter fibres, which have lower electrical resistance.

Axon
Membrane

Passage of
electric current

Unmyelinated axon

Axon
Membrane

Myelin sheath

Passage of
electric current

Myelinated axon

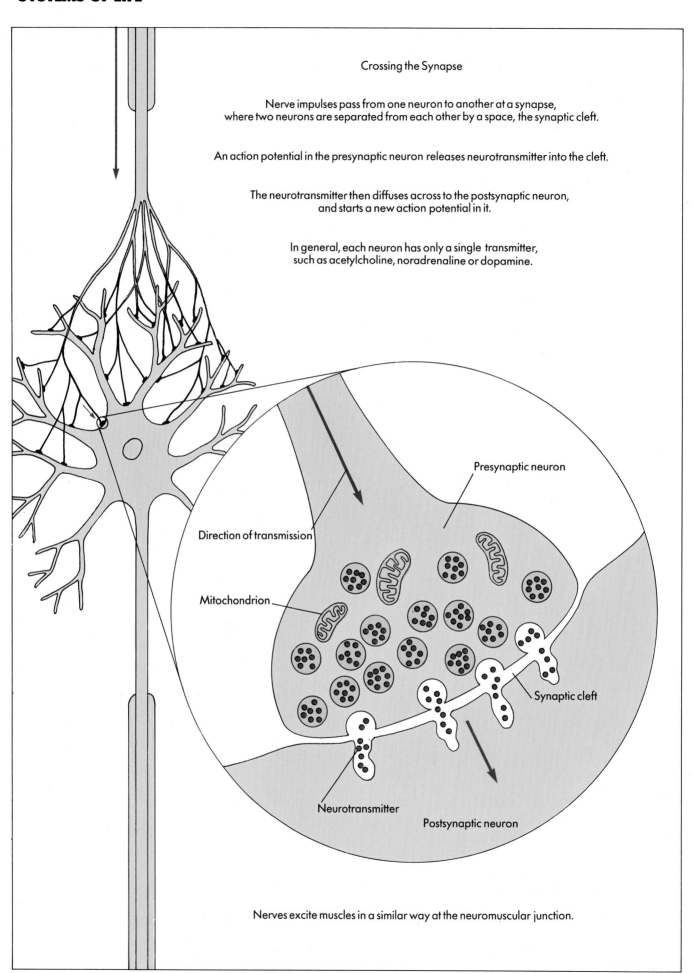

Crossing the Synapse

Nerve impulses pass from one neuron to another at a synapse,
where two neurons are separated from each other by a space, the synaptic cleft.

An action potential in the presynaptic neuron releases neurotransmitter into the cleft.

The neurotransmitter then diffuses across to the postsynaptic neuron,
and starts a new action potential in it.

In general, each neuron has only a single transmitter,
such as acetylcholine, noradrenaline or dopamine.

Presynaptic neuron

Direction of transmission

Mitochondrion

Synaptic cleft

Neurotransmitter

Postsynaptic neuron

Nerves excite muscles in a similar way at the neuromuscular junction.

Nervous tissue is very soft and vulnerable.
When it is destroyed, loss of function can be catastrophic for the person concerned.
The central nervous system is protected from harm by bone, lining membranes and a fluid cushion.

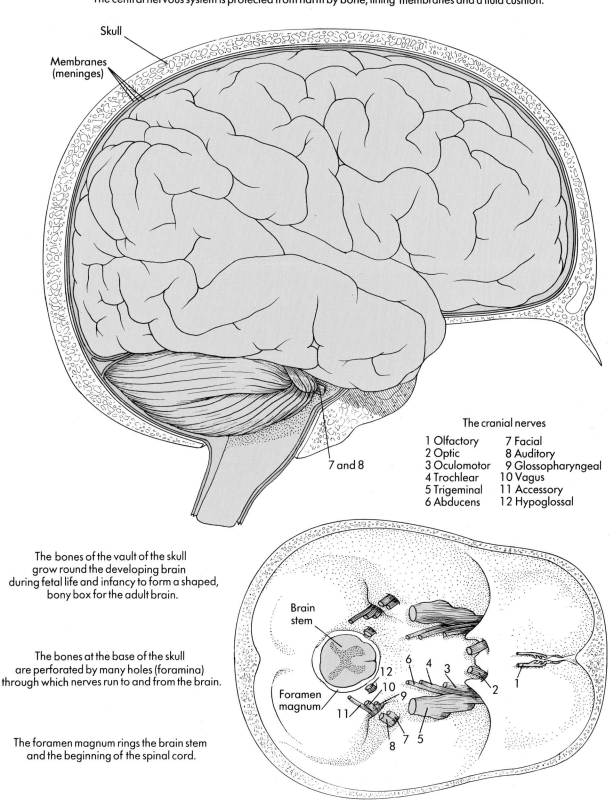

Skull

Membranes
(meninges)

7 and 8

The cranial nerves

1 Olfactory	7 Facial
2 Optic	8 Auditory
3 Oculomotor	9 Glossopharyngeal
4 Trochlear	10 Vagus
5 Trigeminal	11 Accessory
6 Abducens	12 Hypoglossal

The bones of the vault of the skull
grow round the developing brain
during fetal life and infancy to form a shaped,
bony box for the adult brain.

The bones at the base of the skull
are perforated by many holes (foramina)
through which nerves run to and from the brain.

The foramen magnum rings the brain stem
and the beginning of the spinal cord.

Brain
stem

Foramen
magnum

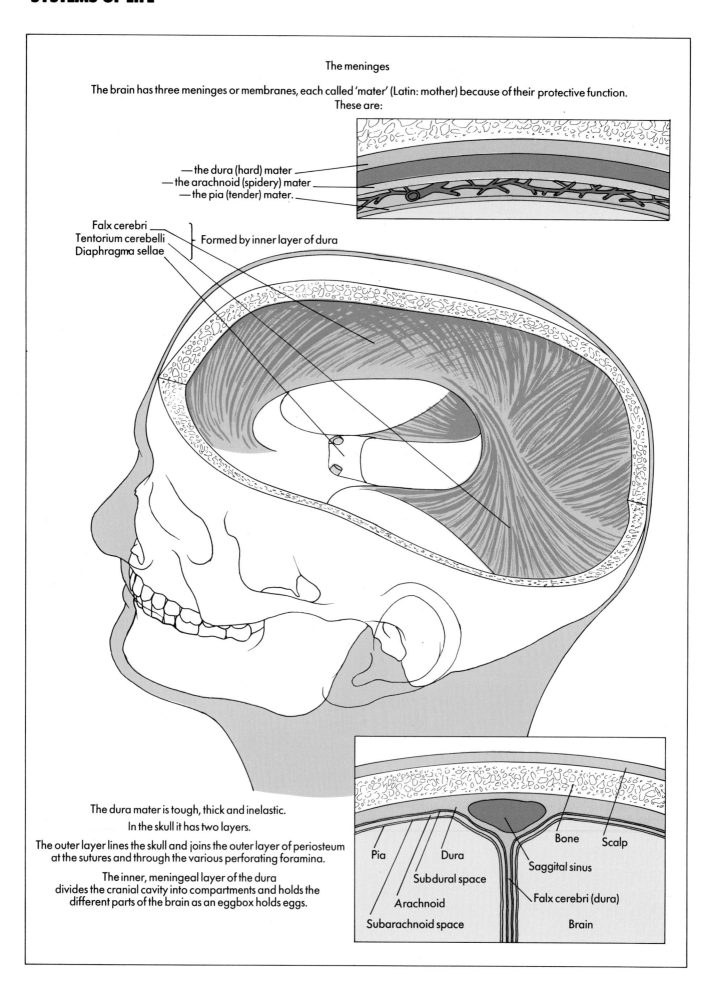

The meninges

The brain has three meninges or membranes, each called 'mater' (Latin: mother) because of their protective function.
These are:

—the dura (hard) mater
—the arachnoid (spidery) mater
—the pia (tender) mater.

Falx cerebri
Tentorium cerebelli   Formed by inner layer of dura
Diaphragma sellae

The dura mater is tough, thick and inelastic.
In the skull it has two layers.
The outer layer lines the skull and joins the outer layer of periosteum at the sutures and through the various perforating foramina.

The inner, meningeal layer of the dura divides the cranial cavity into compartments and holds the different parts of the brain as an eggbox holds eggs.

Pia   Dura   Bone   Scalp
Subdural space   Saggital sinus
Arachnoid   Falx cerebri (dura)
Subarachnoid space   Brain

The spinal dura mater forms a loose sheath for the spinal cord.
It is attached around the edge of the foramen magnum, and is tethered to the vertebrae by small fibrous slips.
Around it the extradural (epidural) space contains a packing of fat, with veins running through it.
Tubular 'sleeves' of dura surround the spinal nerves within the extradural space and as they pass through the vertebral foramina.

The subdural cavity ends at the lower border of the 2nd sacral vertebra.
Below this, the dura clings to the thin filum terminale of the spinal cord, and eventually blends with the periosteum of the coccyx.

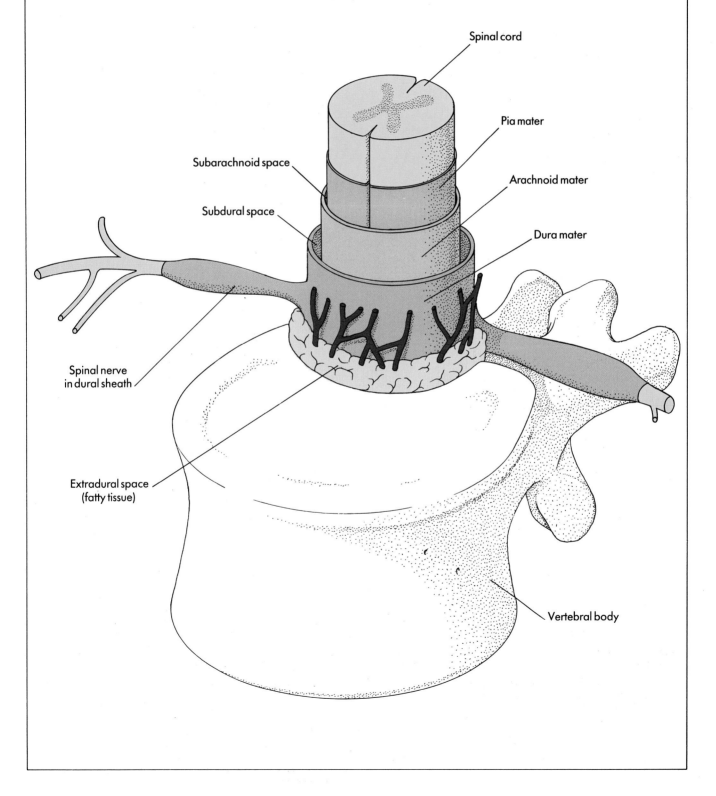

Spinal cord

Pia mater

Subarachnoid space

Arachnoid mater

Subdural space

Dura mater

Spinal nerve
in dural sheath

Extradural space
(fatty tissue)

Vertebral body

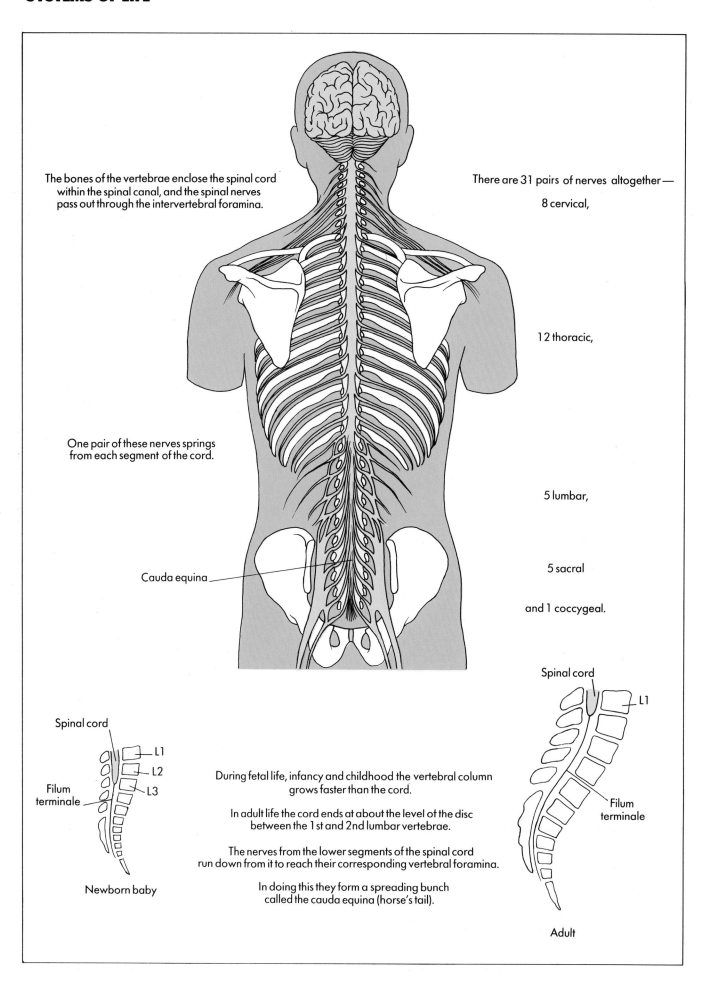

The bones of the vertebrae enclose the spinal cord within the spinal canal, and the spinal nerves pass out through the intervertebral foramina.

There are 31 pairs of nerves altogether —

8 cervical,

12 thoracic,

One pair of these nerves springs from each segment of the cord.

5 lumbar,

5 sacral

and 1 coccygeal.

Cauda equina

Spinal cord

Spinal cord

L1

Spinal cord

L1
L2
L3

Filum
terminale

Filum
terminale

During fetal life, infancy and childhood the vertebral column grows faster than the cord.

In adult life the cord ends at about the level of the disc between the 1st and 2nd lumbar vertebrae.

The nerves from the lower segments of the spinal cord run down from it to reach their corresponding vertebral foramina.

Newborn baby

In doing this they form a spreading bunch called the cauda equina (horse's tail).

Adult

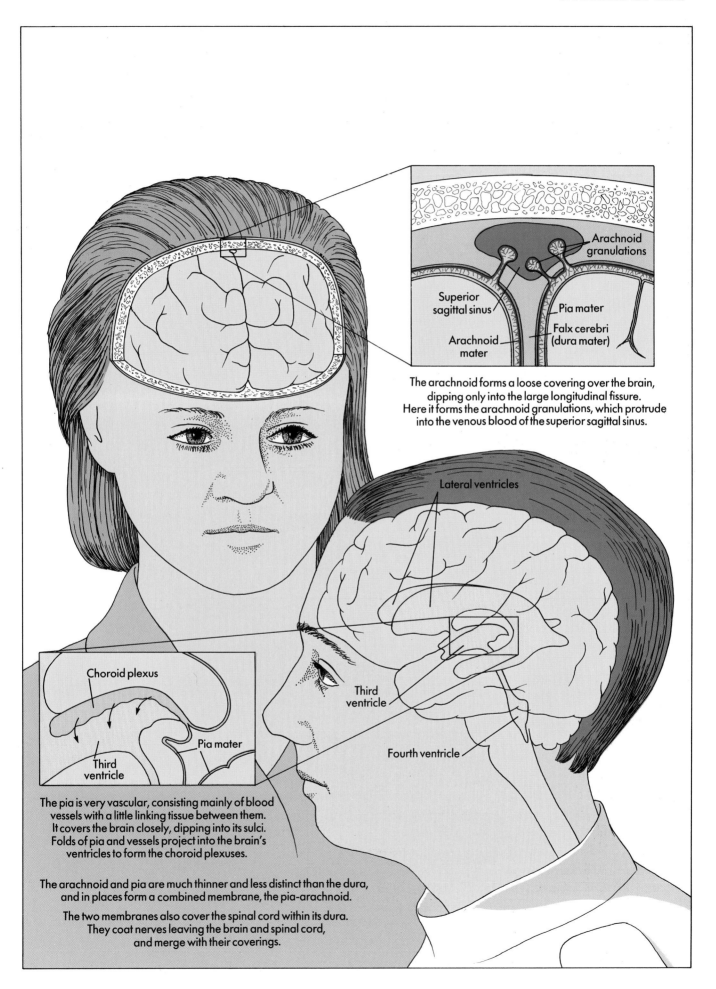

The arachnoid forms a loose covering over the brain, dipping only into the large longitudinal fissure. Here it forms the arachnoid granulations, which protrude into the venous blood of the superior sagittal sinus.

The pia is very vascular, consisting mainly of blood vessels with a little linking tissue between them. It covers the brain closely, dipping into its sulci. Folds of pia and vessels project into the brain's ventricles to form the choroid plexuses.

The arachnoid and pia are much thinner and less distinct than the dura, and in places form a combined membrane, the pia-arachnoid.

The two membranes also cover the spinal cord within its dura. They coat nerves leaving the brain and spinal cord, and merge with their coverings.

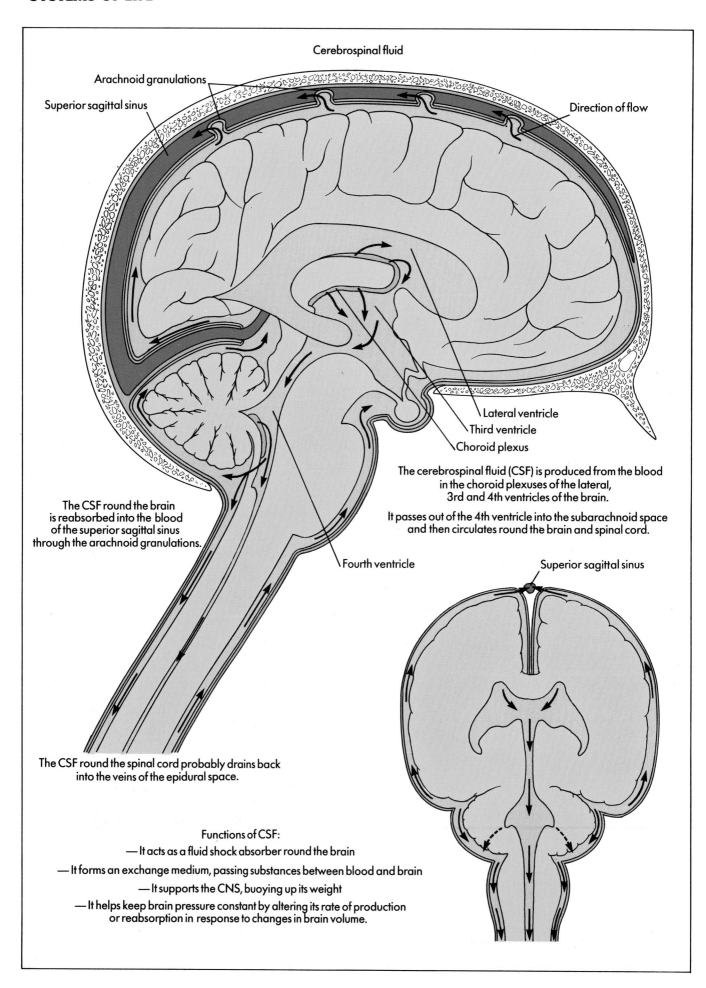

Cerebrospinal fluid

Arachnoid granulations

Superior sagittal sinus

Direction of flow

Lateral ventricle
Third ventricle
Choroid plexus

The cerebrospinal fluid (CSF) is produced from the blood
in the choroid plexuses of the lateral,
3rd and 4th ventricles of the brain.

It passes out of the 4th ventricle into the subarachnoid space
and then circulates round the brain and spinal cord.

The CSF round the brain
is reabsorbed into the blood
of the superior sagittal sinus
through the arachnoid granulations.

Fourth ventricle

Superior sagittal sinus

The CSF round the spinal cord probably drains back
into the veins of the epidural space.

Functions of CSF:
— It acts as a fluid shock absorber round the brain

— It forms an exchange medium, passing substances between blood and brain

— It supports the CNS, buoying up its weight

— It helps keep brain pressure constant by altering its rate of production
or reabsorption in response to changes in brain volume.

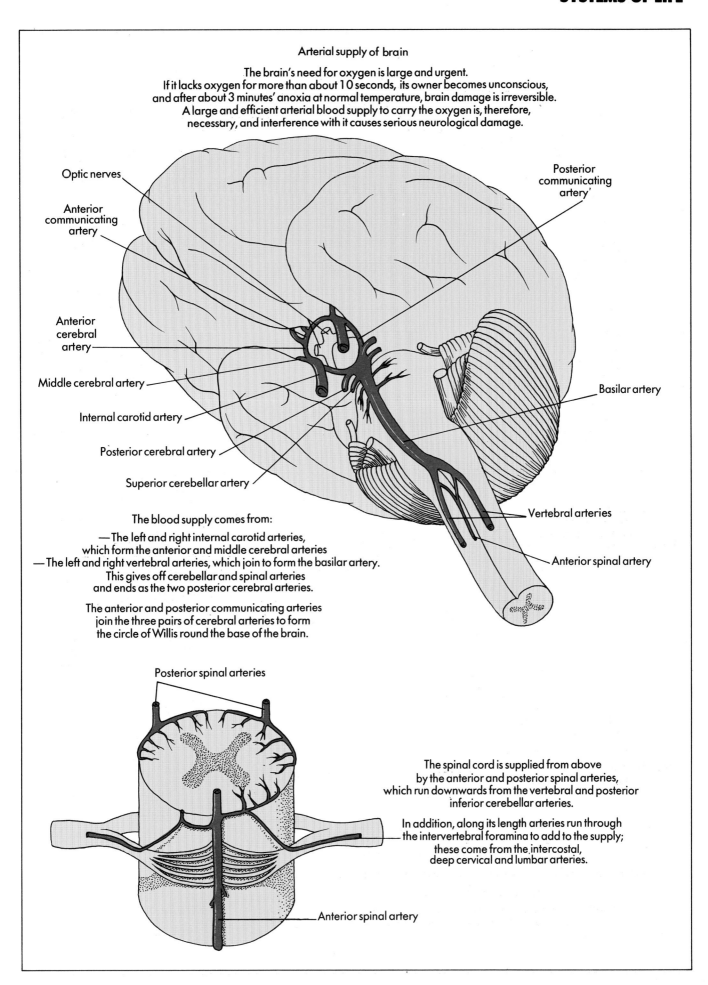

Arterial supply of brain

The brain's need for oxygen is large and urgent.
If it lacks oxygen for more than about 10 seconds, its owner becomes unconscious,
and after about 3 minutes' anoxia at normal temperature, brain damage is irreversible.
A large and efficient arterial blood supply to carry the oxygen is, therefore,
necessary, and interference with it causes serious neurological damage.

Optic nerves

Anterior communicating artery

Anterior cerebral artery

Middle cerebral artery

Internal carotid artery

Posterior cerebral artery

Superior cerebellar artery

Posterior communicating artery'

Basilar artery

Vertebral arteries

Anterior spinal artery

The blood supply comes from:

—The left and right internal carotid arteries,
which form the anterior and middle cerebral arteries
—The left and right vertebral arteries, which join to form the basilar artery.
This gives off cerebellar and spinal arteries
and ends as the two posterior cerebral arteries.

The anterior and posterior communicating arteries
join the three pairs of cerebral arteries to form
the circle of Willis round the base of the brain.

Posterior spinal arteries

The spinal cord is supplied from above
by the anterior and posterior spinal arteries,
which run downwards from the vertebral and posterior
inferior cerebellar arteries.

In addition, along its length arteries run through
the intervertebral foramina to add to the supply;
these come from the intercostal,
deep cervical and lumbar arteries.

Anterior spinal artery

55

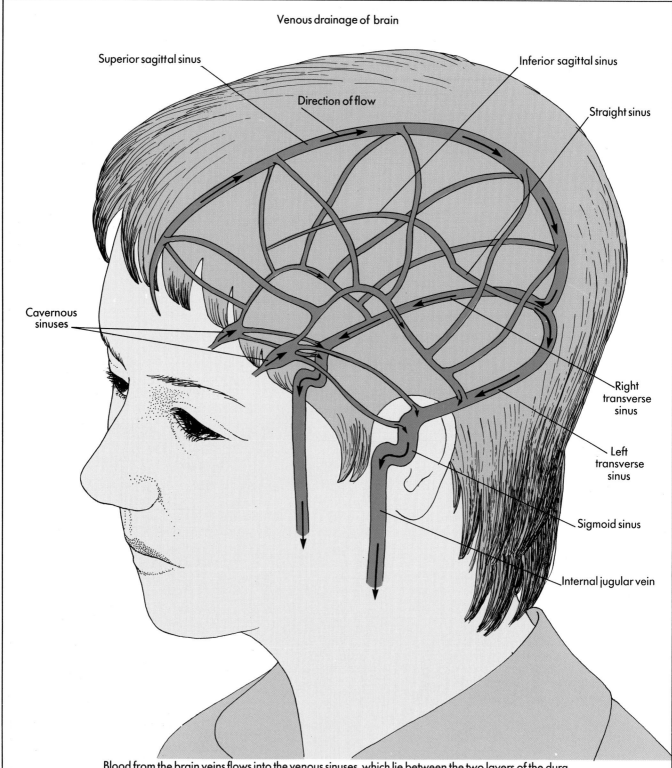

Venous drainage of brain

Superior sagittal sinus

Inferior sagittal sinus

Direction of flow

Straight sinus

Cavernous sinuses

Right transverse sinus

Left transverse sinus

Sigmoid sinus

Internal jugular vein

Blood from the brain veins flows into the venous sinuses, which lie between the two layers of the dura.
The sinuses are lined with endothelium and have no valves.
Blood circulates through them partly under gravity and partly because it is pushed from behind by the force of the arterial blood.

Blood from the superior sagittal sinus flows into one transverse sinus,
usually the right, and that from the straight sinus into the other, usually the left.
Blood from the cavernous sinus, from the eye and its socket
and some tissues of the face as well as part of the brain, drains into the transverse sinus.
This becomes the sigmoid sinus and then the internal jugular vein.

The veins of the spinal cord form a plexus in the pia mater.
They join together near the base of the skull to form trunks which end in the inferior cerebellar veins or the venous sinuses.
Spinal cord veins also communicate with the veins draining the vertebrae.

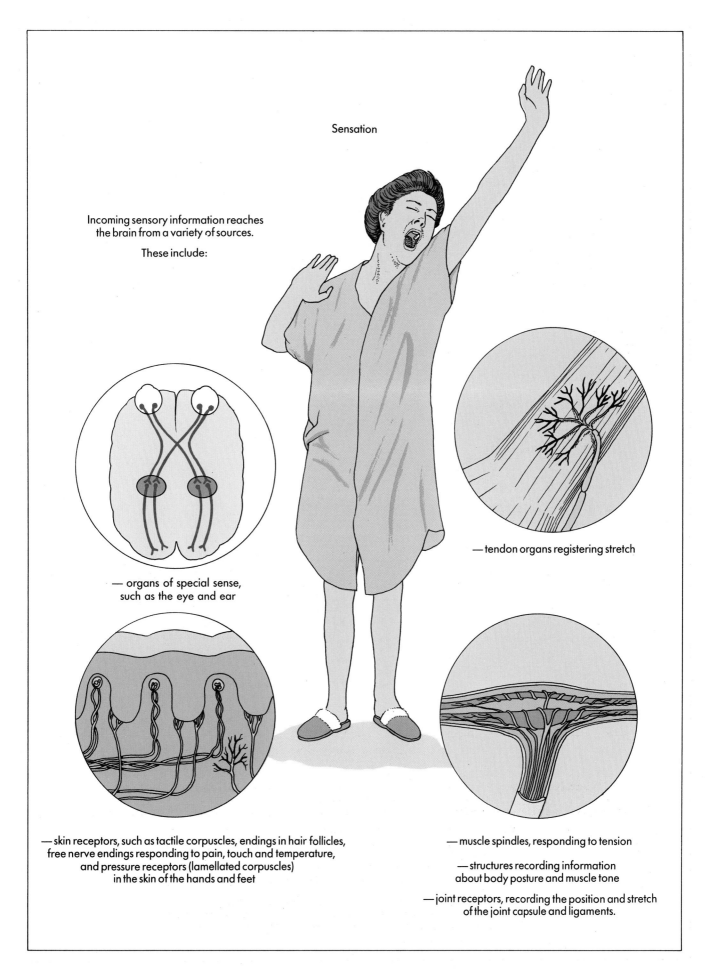

Sensation

Incoming sensory information reaches
the brain from a variety of sources.

These include:

— organs of special sense,
such as the eye and ear

—tendon organs registering stretch

—skin receptors, such as tactile corpuscles, endings in hair follicles,
free nerve endings responding to pain, touch and temperature,
and pressure receptors (lamellated corpuscles)
in the skin of the hands and feet

— muscle spindles, responding to tension

— structures recording information
about body posture and muscle tone

—joint receptors, recording the position and stretch
of the joint capsule and ligaments.

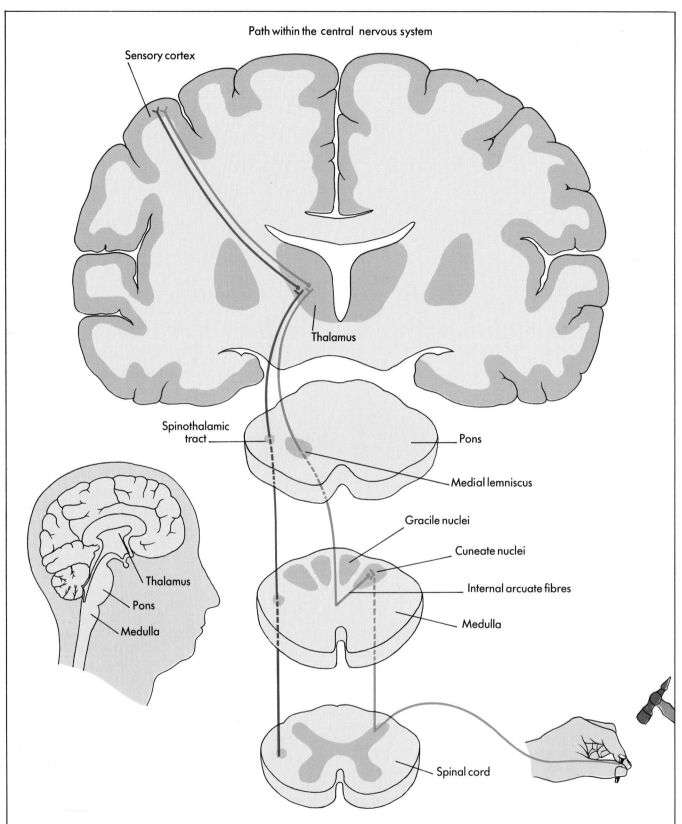

Path within the central nervous system

Sensory cortex

Thalamus

Spinothalamic tract

Pons

Medial lemniscus

Gracile nuclei

Cuneate nuclei

Internal arcuate fibres

Medulla

Thalamus

Pons

Medulla

Spinal cord

Sensory information passes to the spinal cord by its dorsal root. It then travels up the spinal cord towards the brain.
Fibres carrying vibration sense, joint position sense and some touch sensation form the gracile and cuneate tracts.
These run up the cord on the same side that the fibres entered it till they reach the cuneate and gracile nuclei in the lower medulla.
Here the fibres cross the midline as the internal arcuate fibres.
Then they move laterally in the pons and are called the medial lemniscus, which joins the spinothalamic tract.
Both sets of fibres synapse in the thalamus and their information is relayed to the sensory cortex.

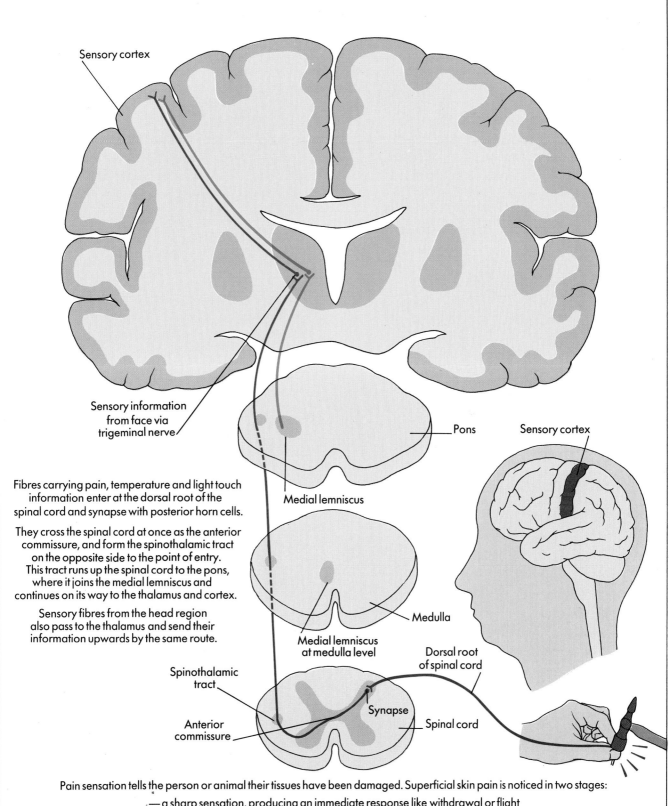

Sensory cortex

Sensory information
from face via
trigeminal nerve

Pons

Sensory cortex

Medial lemniscus

Fibres carrying pain, temperature and light touch
information enter at the dorsal root of the
spinal cord and synapse with posterior horn cells.

They cross the spinal cord at once as the anterior
commissure, and form the spinothalamic tract
on the opposite side to the point of entry.
This tract runs up the spinal cord to the pons,
where it joins the medial lemniscus and
continues on its way to the thalamus and cortex.

Sensory fibres from the head region
also pass to the thalamus and send their
information upwards by the same route.

Medulla

Medial lemniscus
at medulla level

Dorsal root
of spinal cord

Spinothalamic
tract

Synapse

Spinal cord

Anterior
commissure

Pain sensation tells the person or animal their tissues have been damaged. Superficial skin pain is noticed in two stages:

— a sharp sensation, producing an immediate response like withdrawal or flight

— a continuous ache, which reminds the individual to take special care of the damaged part.

Pain receptors do not adapt to persistent stimuli, but go on recording them.

Pain fibres from the skin and the viscera run together in the spinothalamic tract.
Because of this, pain from internal organs is often perceived as if it were coming from the skin areas
supplied by the same segment of the spinal cord. This is called referred pain.
Examples are: pain from irritation of the diaphragm being transferred to the tip of the shoulder;
pain from the womb being felt in the back or labia.

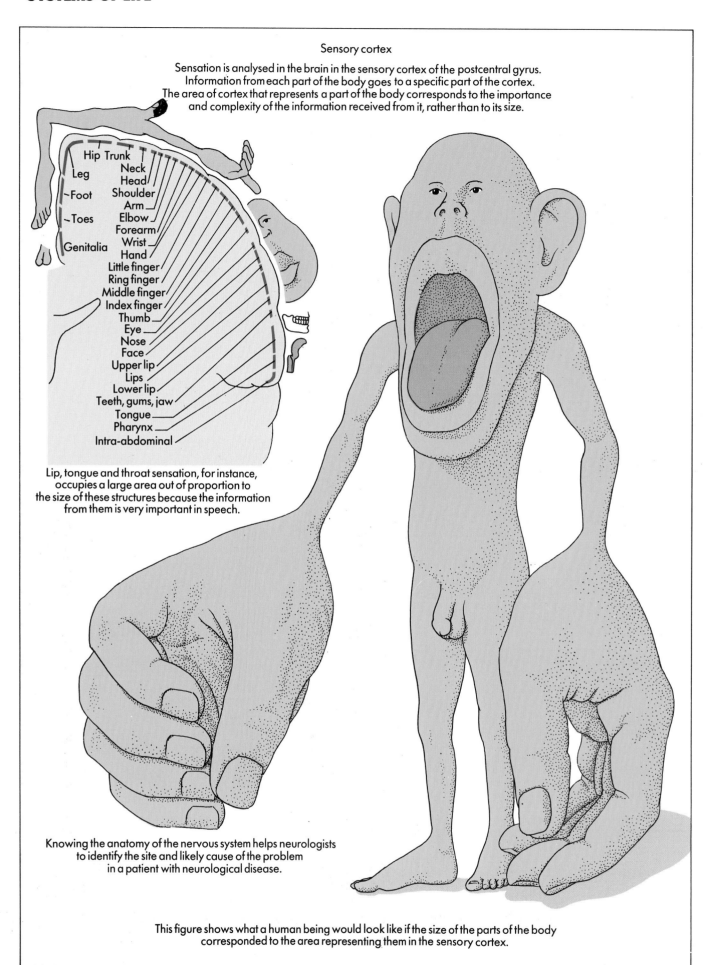

Sensory cortex

Sensation is analysed in the brain in the sensory cortex of the postcentral gyrus. Information from each part of the body goes to a specific part of the cortex. The area of cortex that represents a part of the body corresponds to the importance and complexity of the information received from it, rather than to its size.

Hip Trunk
Leg
Neck
Head
Foot
Shoulder
Arm
Toes
Elbow
Forearm
Wrist
Genitalia
Hand
Little finger
Ring finger
Middle finger
Index finger
Thumb
Eye
Nose
Face
Upper lip
Lips
Lower lip
Teeth, gums, jaw
Tongue
Pharynx
Intra-abdominal

Lip, tongue and throat sensation, for instance, occupies a large area out of proportion to the size of these structures because the information from them is very important in speech.

Knowing the anatomy of the nervous system helps neurologists to identify the site and likely cause of the problem in a patient with neurological disease.

This figure shows what a human being would look like if the size of the parts of the body corresponded to the area representing them in the sensory cortex.

Motor function

Motor activity involves both:

—willed, voluntary movements,
like the fine hand movements
of playing a musical instrument.
These take place against a
background of postural activity

—postural control, the co-ordination of the muscles involved in maintaining balance and posture.
This is largely unconscious, ie, is not 'thought about' at the conscious level.

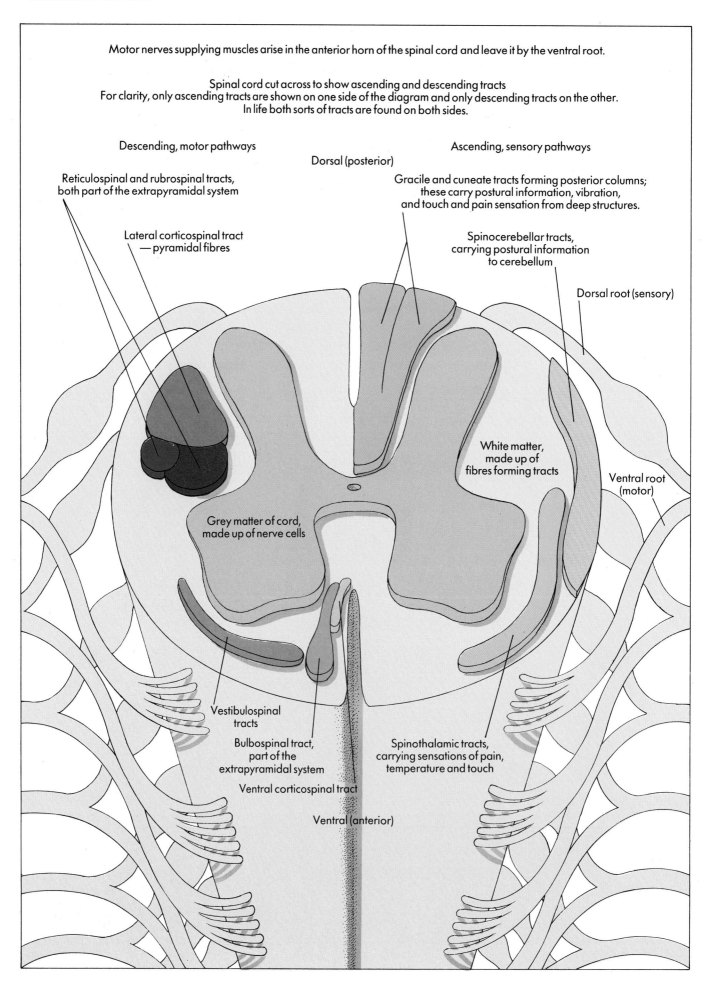

Motor nerves supplying muscles arise in the anterior horn of the spinal cord and leave it by the ventral root.

Spinal cord cut across to show ascending and descending tracts
For clarity, only ascending tracts are shown on one side of the diagram and only descending tracts on the other.
In life both sorts of tracts are found on both sides.

Descending, motor pathways

Ascending, sensory pathways

Dorsal (posterior)

Reticulospinal and rubrospinal tracts, both part of the extrapyramidal system

Gracile and cuneate tracts forming posterior columns; these carry postural information, vibration, and touch and pain sensation from deep structures.

Lateral corticospinal tract — pyramidal fibres

Spinocerebellar tracts, carrying postural information to cerebellum

Dorsal root (sensory)

White matter, made up of fibres forming tracts

Ventral root (motor)

Grey matter of cord, made up of nerve cells

Vestibulospinal tracts

Bulbospinal tract, part of the extrapyramidal system

Spinothalamic tracts, carrying sensations of pain, temperature and touch

Ventral corticospinal tract

Ventral (anterior)

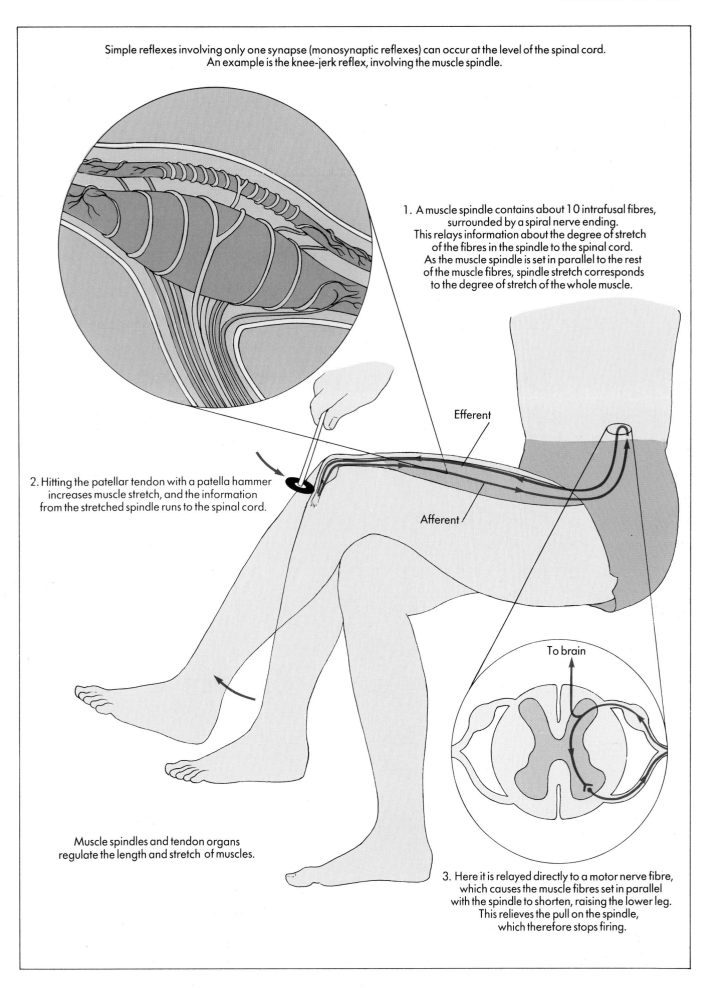

Simple reflexes involving only one synapse (monosynaptic reflexes) can occur at the level of the spinal cord. An example is the knee-jerk reflex, involving the muscle spindle.

1. A muscle spindle contains about 10 intrafusal fibres, surrounded by a spiral nerve ending. This relays information about the degree of stretch of the fibres in the spindle to the spinal cord. As the muscle spindle is set in parallel to the rest of the muscle fibres, spindle stretch corresponds to the degree of stretch of the whole muscle.

Efferent

Afferent

2. Hitting the patellar tendon with a patella hammer increases muscle stretch, and the information from the stretched spindle runs to the spinal cord.

To brain

Muscle spindles and tendon organs regulate the length and stretch of muscles.

3. Here it is relayed directly to a motor nerve fibre, which causes the muscle fibres set in parallel with the spindle to shorten, raising the lower leg. This relieves the pull on the spindle, which therefore stops firing.

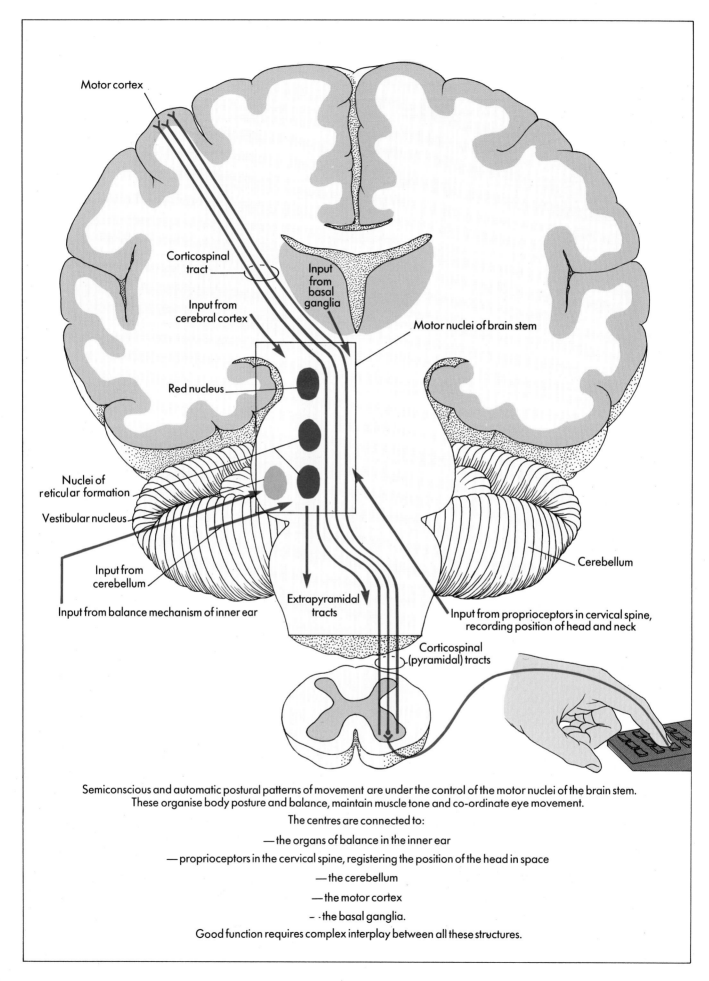

Motor cortex

Corticospinal tract

Input from basal ganglia

Input from cerebral cortex

Motor nuclei of brain stem

Red nucleus

Nuclei of reticular formation

Vestibular nucleus

Input from cerebellum

Input from balance mechanism of inner ear

Extrapyramidal tracts

Cerebellum

Input from proprioceptors in cervical spine, recording position of head and neck

Corticospinal (pyramidal) tracts

Semiconscious and automatic postural patterns of movement are under the control of the motor nuclei of the brain stem. These organise body posture and balance, maintain muscle tone and co-ordinate eye movement.

The centres are connected to:

—the organs of balance in the inner ear

—proprioceptors in the cervical spine, registering the position of the head in space

—the cerebellum

—the motor cortex

- ·the basal ganglia.

Good function requires complex interplay between all these structures.

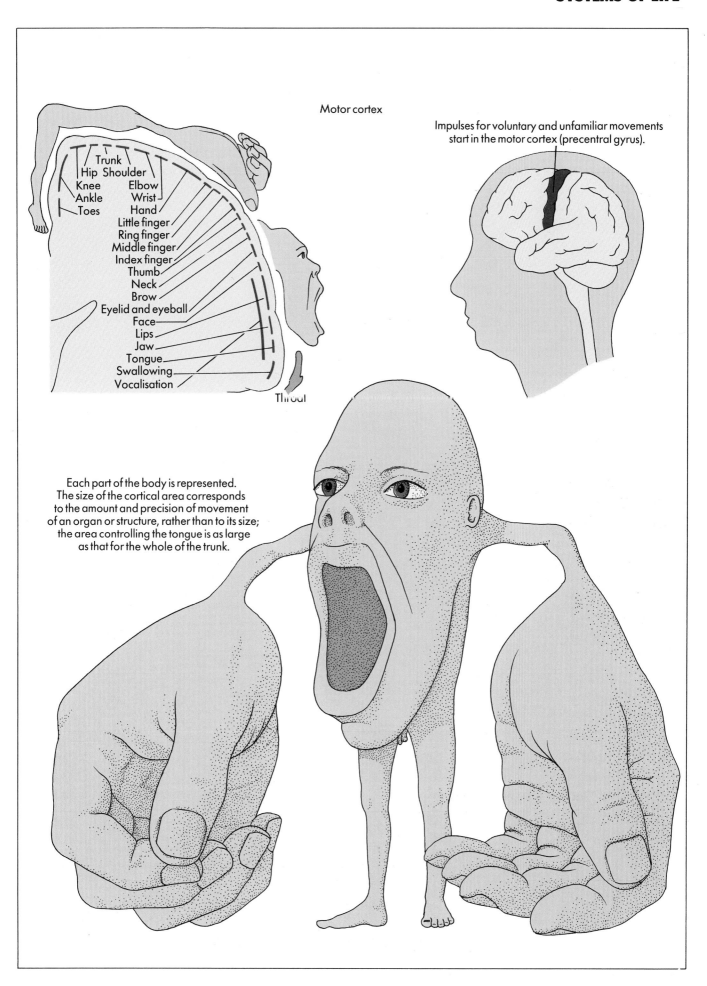

Motor cortex

Trunk
Hip Shoulder
Knee Elbow
Ankle Wrist
Toes Hand
Little finger
Ring finger
Middle finger
Index finger
Thumb
Neck
Brow
Eyelid and eyeball
Face
Lips
Jaw
Tongue
Swallowing
Vocalisation

Throat

Impulses for voluntary and unfamiliar movements start in the motor cortex (precentral gyrus).

Each part of the body is represented. The size of the cortical area corresponds to the amount and precision of movement of an organ or structure, rather than to its size; the area controlling the tongue is as large as that for the whole of the trunk.

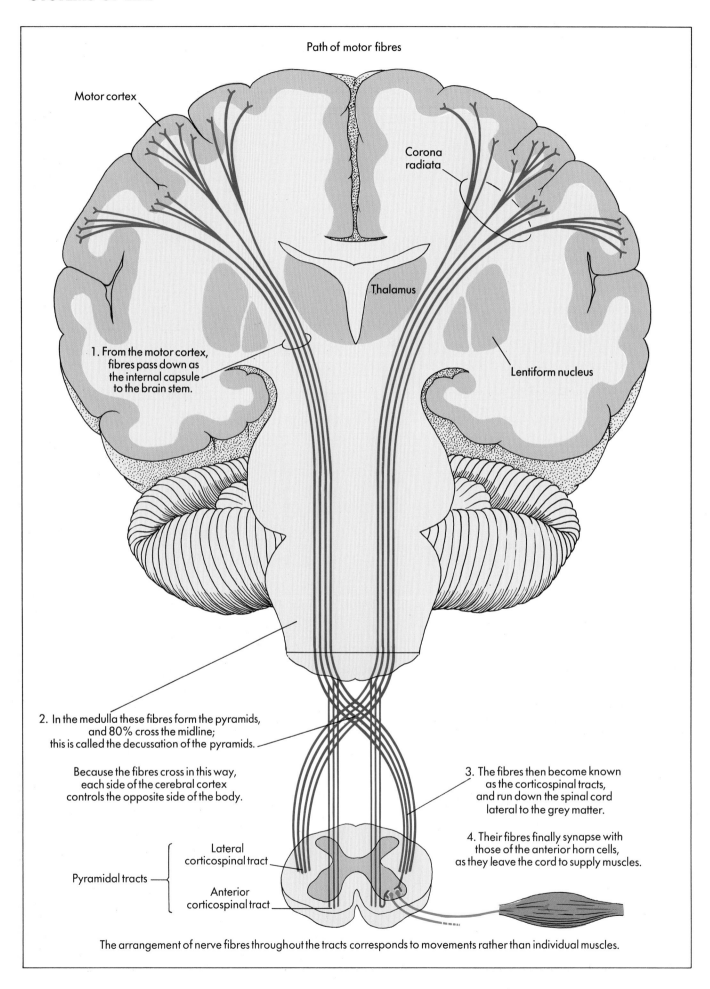

Path of motor fibres

Motor cortex

Corona radiata

Thalamus

1. From the motor cortex, fibres pass down as the internal capsule to the brain stem.

Lentiform nucleus

2. In the medulla these fibres form the pyramids, and 80% cross the midline; this is called the decussation of the pyramids.

Because the fibres cross in this way, each side of the cerebral cortex controls the opposite side of the body.

3. The fibres then become known as the corticospinal tracts, and run down the spinal cord lateral to the grey matter.

4. Their fibres finally synapse with those of the anterior horn cells, as they leave the cord to supply muscles.

Lateral corticospinal tract

Pyramidal tracts

Anterior corticospinal tract

The arrangement of nerve fibres throughout the tracts corresponds to movements rather than individual muscles.

66

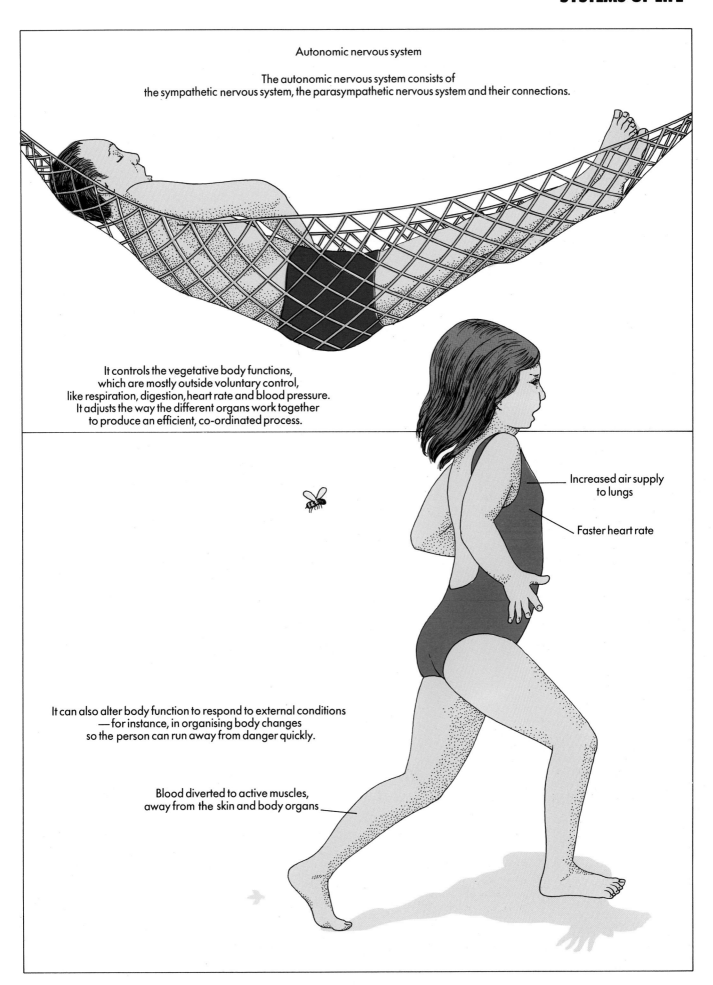

Autonomic nervous system

The autonomic nervous system consists of
the sympathetic nervous system, the parasympathetic nervous system and their connections.

It controls the vegetative body functions,
which are mostly outside voluntary control,
like respiration, digestion, heart rate and blood pressure.
It adjusts the way the different organs work together
to produce an efficient, co-ordinated process.

Increased air supply
to lungs

Faster heart rate

It can also alter body function to respond to external conditions
— for instance, in organising body changes
so the person can run away from danger quickly.

Blood diverted to active muscles,
away from the skin and body organs

67

The autonomic nervous system supplies:

—smooth muscle, in bronchioles, gut, blood vessels, uterus and bladder
—cardiac muscle
—glands.

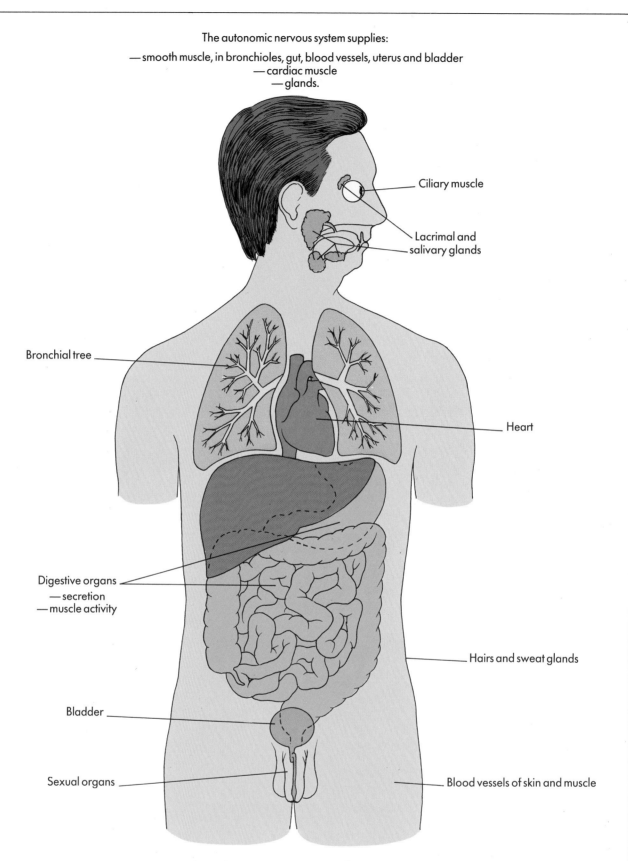

Ciliary muscle

Lacrimal and
salivary glands

Bronchial tree

Heart

Digestive organs
—secretion
—muscle activity

Hairs and sweat glands

Bladder

Sexual organs

Blood vessels of skin and muscle

Special autonomic nerves run to the viscera,
but otherwise autonomic efferent nerves to blood vessels and skin run in the peripheral somatic nerves.

Autonomic afferents transmit sensation from the viscera to the CNS;
information about distension of the rectum and bladder and visceral pain probably travel in this way,
as do less well defined sensations such as hunger and nausea.

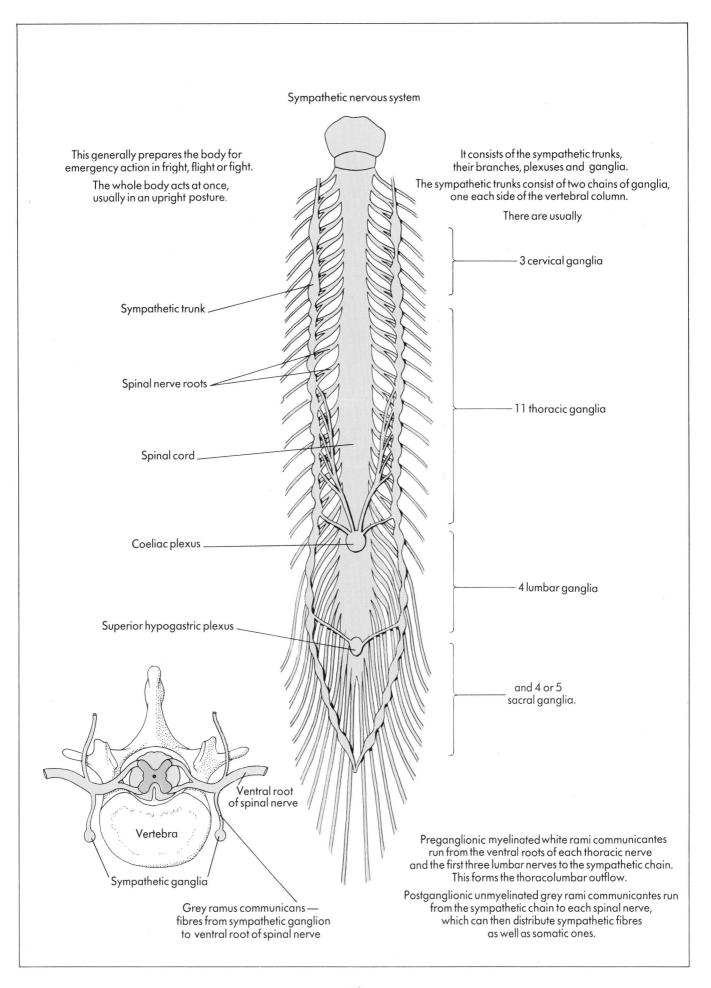

Sympathetic nervous system

This generally prepares the body for emergency action in fright, flight or fight.

The whole body acts at once, usually in an upright posture.

It consists of the sympathetic trunks, their branches, plexuses and ganglia.

The sympathetic trunks consist of two chains of ganglia, one each side of the vertebral column.

There are usually

3 cervical ganglia

Sympathetic trunk

Spinal nerve roots

11 thoracic ganglia

Spinal cord

Coeliac plexus

4 lumbar ganglia

Superior hypogastric plexus

and 4 or 5 sacral ganglia.

Ventral root of spinal nerve

Vertebra

Sympathetic ganglia

Grey ramus communicans — fibres from sympathetic ganglion to ventral root of spinal nerve

Preganglionic myelinated white rami communicantes run from the ventral roots of each thoracic nerve and the first three lumbar nerves to the sympathetic chain. This forms the thoracolumbar outflow.

Postganglionic unmyelinated grey rami communicantes run from the sympathetic chain to each spinal nerve, which can then distribute sympathetic fibres as well as somatic ones.

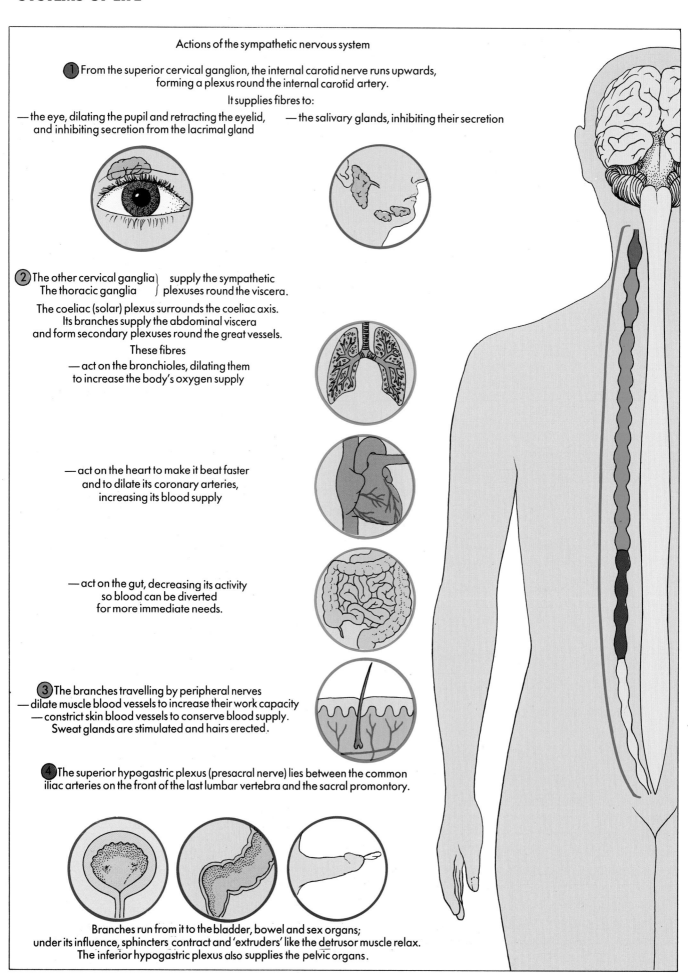

Actions of the sympathetic nervous system

1 From the superior cervical ganglion, the internal carotid nerve runs upwards, forming a plexus round the internal carotid artery.

It supplies fibres to:

— the eye, dilating the pupil and retracting the eyelid, and inhibiting secretion from the lacrimal gland

— the salivary glands, inhibiting their secretion

2 The other cervical ganglia ⎫ supply the sympathetic
The thoracic ganglia ⎭ plexuses round the viscera.

The coeliac (solar) plexus surrounds the coeliac axis. Its branches supply the abdominal viscera and form secondary plexuses round the great vessels.

These fibres
— act on the bronchioles, dilating them to increase the body's oxygen supply

— act on the heart to make it beat faster and to dilate its coronary arteries, increasing its blood supply

— act on the gut, decreasing its activity so blood can be diverted for more immediate needs.

3 The branches travelling by peripheral nerves
— dilate muscle blood vessels to increase their work capacity
— constrict skin blood vessels to conserve blood supply. Sweat glands are stimulated and hairs erected.

4 The superior hypogastric plexus (presacral nerve) lies between the common iliac arteries on the front of the last lumbar vertebra and the sacral promontory.

Branches run from it to the bladder, bowel and sex organs; under its influence, sphincters contract and 'extruders' like the detrusor muscle relax. The inferior hypogastric plexus also supplies the pelvic organs.

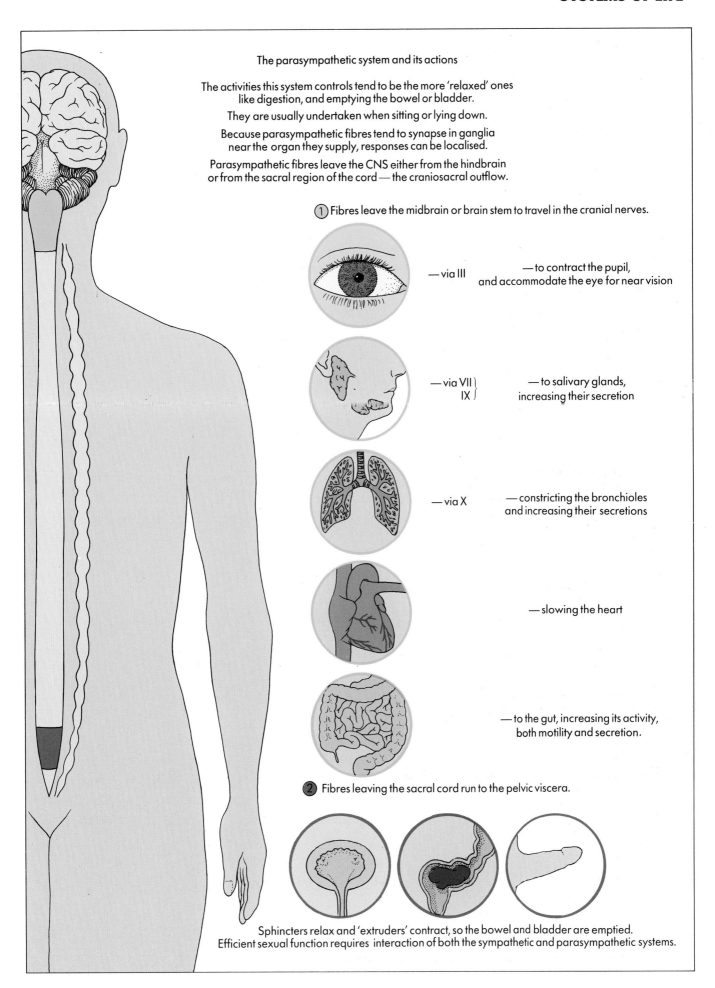

The parasympathetic system and its actions

The activities this system controls tend to be the more 'relaxed' ones like digestion, and emptying the bowel or bladder.

They are usually undertaken when sitting or lying down.

Because parasympathetic fibres tend to synapse in ganglia near the organ they supply, responses can be localised.

Parasympathetic fibres leave the CNS either from the hindbrain or from the sacral region of the cord — the craniosacral outflow.

① Fibres leave the midbrain or brain stem to travel in the cranial nerves.

— via III   — to contract the pupil, and accommodate the eye for near vision

— via VII
    IX   — to salivary glands, increasing their secretion

— via X   — constricting the bronchioles and increasing their secretions

— slowing the heart

— to the gut, increasing its activity, both motility and secretion.

② Fibres leaving the sacral cord run to the pelvic viscera.

Sphincters relax and 'extruders' contract, so the bowel and bladder are emptied. Efficient sexual function requires interaction of both the sympathetic and parasympathetic systems.

SYSTEMS OF LIFE

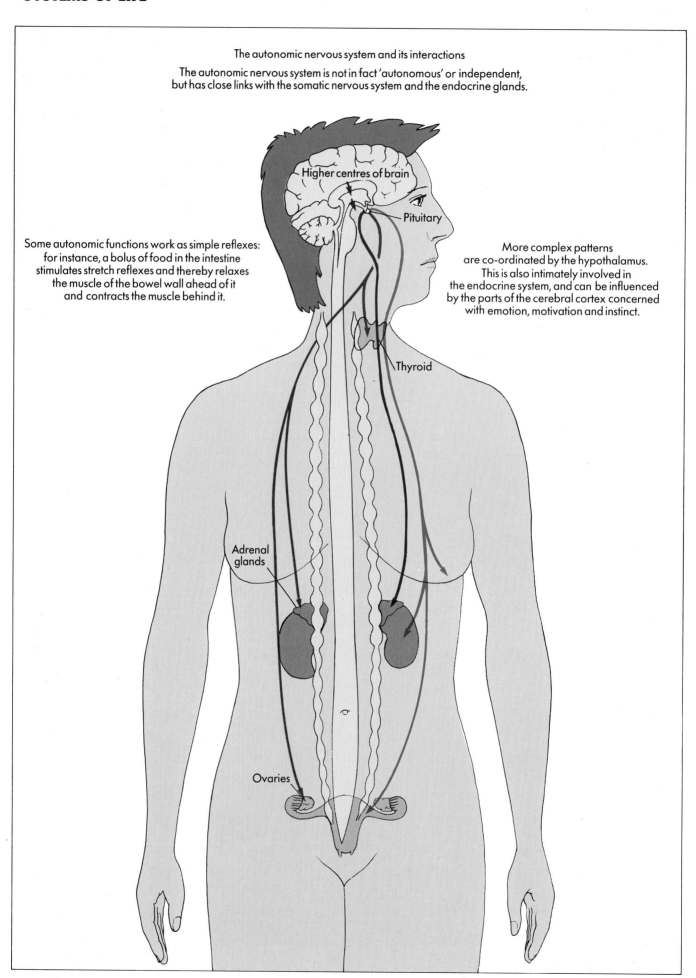

The autonomic nervous system and its interactions

The autonomic nervous system is not in fact 'autonomous' or independent,
but has close links with the somatic nervous system and the endocrine glands.

Higher centres of brain

Pituitary

Some autonomic functions work as simple reflexes:
for instance, a bolus of food in the intestine
stimulates stretch reflexes and thereby relaxes
the muscle of the bowel wall ahead of it
and contracts the muscle behind it.

More complex patterns
are co-ordinated by the hypothalamus.
This is also intimately involved in
the endocrine system, and can be influenced
by the parts of the cerebral cortex concerned
with emotion, motivation and instinct.

Thyroid

Adrenal
glands

Ovaries

72